Maths Practice for

Ages 6–7

This book belongs to:

....

SCHOLASTIC

Maths Year 2, Book 1

Scholastic Education, an imprint of Scholastic Ltd
Book End, Range Road, Witney, Oxfordshire, OX29 0YD
Registered office: Westfield Road, Southam, Warwickshire CV47 0RA
www.scholastic.co.uk

3 4 5 6 7 8 9   6 7 8 9 0 1 2 3 4 5

British Library Cataloguing-in-Publication Data
A catalogue record for this book is available from the British Library.

ISBN 978-1407-14207-4
Printed in Malaysia

Editorial
Rachel Morgan, Robin Hunt, Kate Baxter, Lesley Fletcher,
Sara Wiegand, Mark Walker

Design
Scholastic Design Team: Neil Salt, Nicolle Thomas
and Oxford Designers & Illustrators Ltd

Cover Design
Neil Salt

Illustration
Cathy Hughes

Contents

Why buy this book?

This series has been designed to support the introduction of the new National Curriculum in schools in England. The new curriculum is more challenging in mathematics and includes the requirement for children's understanding to be secure before moving on. These practice books will help your child revise and practise all of the skills they will learn at school, and including some topics they might not have encountered previously.

How to use this book

- The content is divided into National Curriculum topics (for example, Addition and subtraction, Fractions and so on). Find out what your child is doing in school and dip into the relevant practice activities as required.
- Share the activities and support your child if necessary using the helpful quick tips at the top of most pages.
- Keep the working time short and come back to an activity if your child finds it too difficult. Ask your child to note any areas of difficulty at the back of the book. Don't worry if your child does not 'get' a concept first time, as children learn at different rates and content is likely to be covered throughout the school year.
- Check your child's answers using the answers section at the back of the book.
- Give lots of encouragement and tick off the progress chart as your child completes each chapter.

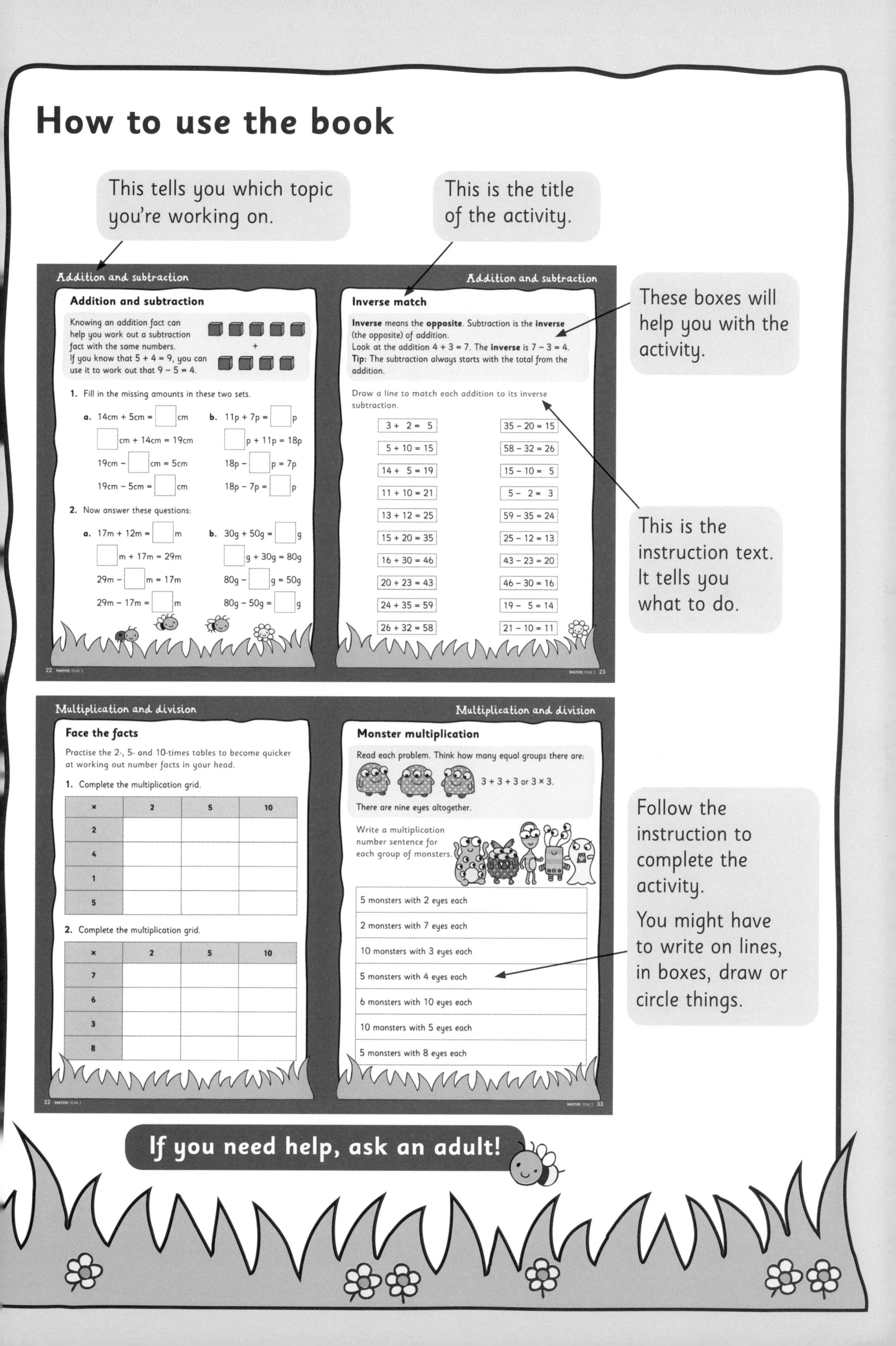
How to use the book
This tells you which topic you're working on.
This is the title of the activity.
These boxes will help you with the activity.
This is the instruction text. It tells you what to do.
Follow the instruction to complete the activity.
You might have to write on lines, in boxes, draw or circle things.
Addition and subtraction
Addition and subtraction
Knowing an addition fact can help you work out a subtraction fact with the same numbers. If you know that 5 + 4 = 9, you can use it to work out that 9 – 5 = 4.
1. Fill in the missing amounts in these two sets.
2. Now answer these questions:
Inverse match
Inverse means the opposite. Subtraction is the inverse (the opposite) of addition.
Look at the addition 4 + 3 = 7. The inverse is 7 – 3 = 4.
Tip: The subtraction always starts with the total from the addition.
Draw a line to match each addition to its inverse subtraction.
Multiplication and division
Face the facts
Practise the 2-, 5- and 10-times tables to become quicker at working out number facts in your head.
1. Complete the multiplication grid.
2. Complete the multiplication grid.
Monster multiplication
Read each problem. Think how many equal groups there are:
3 + 3 + 3 or 3 × 3.
There are nine eyes altogether.
Write a multiplication number sentence for each group of monsters.
If you need help, ask an adult!

Hopscotch counting

To work out the missing numbers, ask: What steps are you counting in?
Tip: If you are counting in 10s, the 1s digit stays the same: 12, 22, 32, 42...

Fill in the missing numbers on these hopscotch frames.

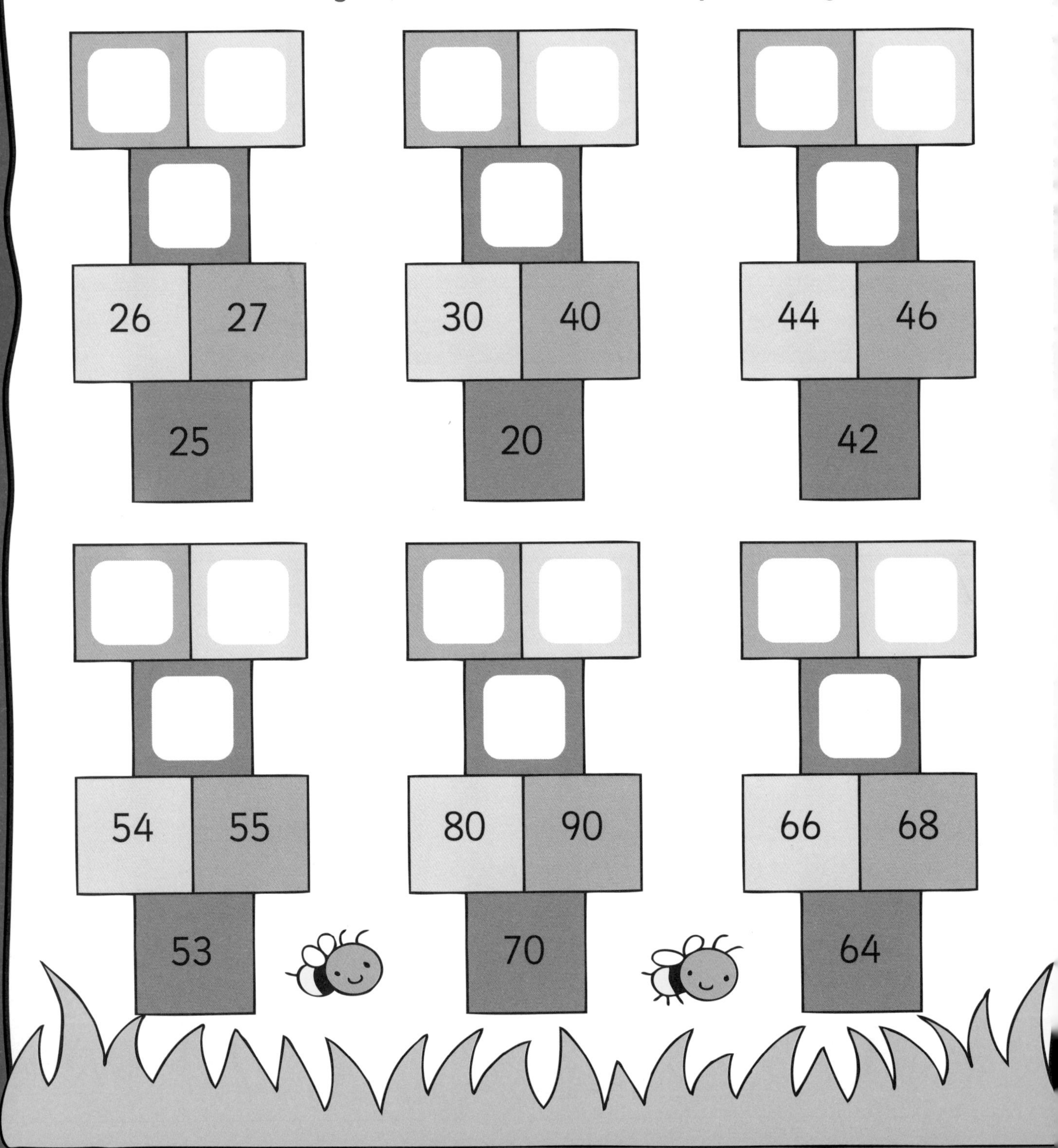

Counting on and back

The first number below gives you the rule to follow for each pattern.
You will need to count on or count back from the starting number.

Write the missing numbers. The first one is done for you.

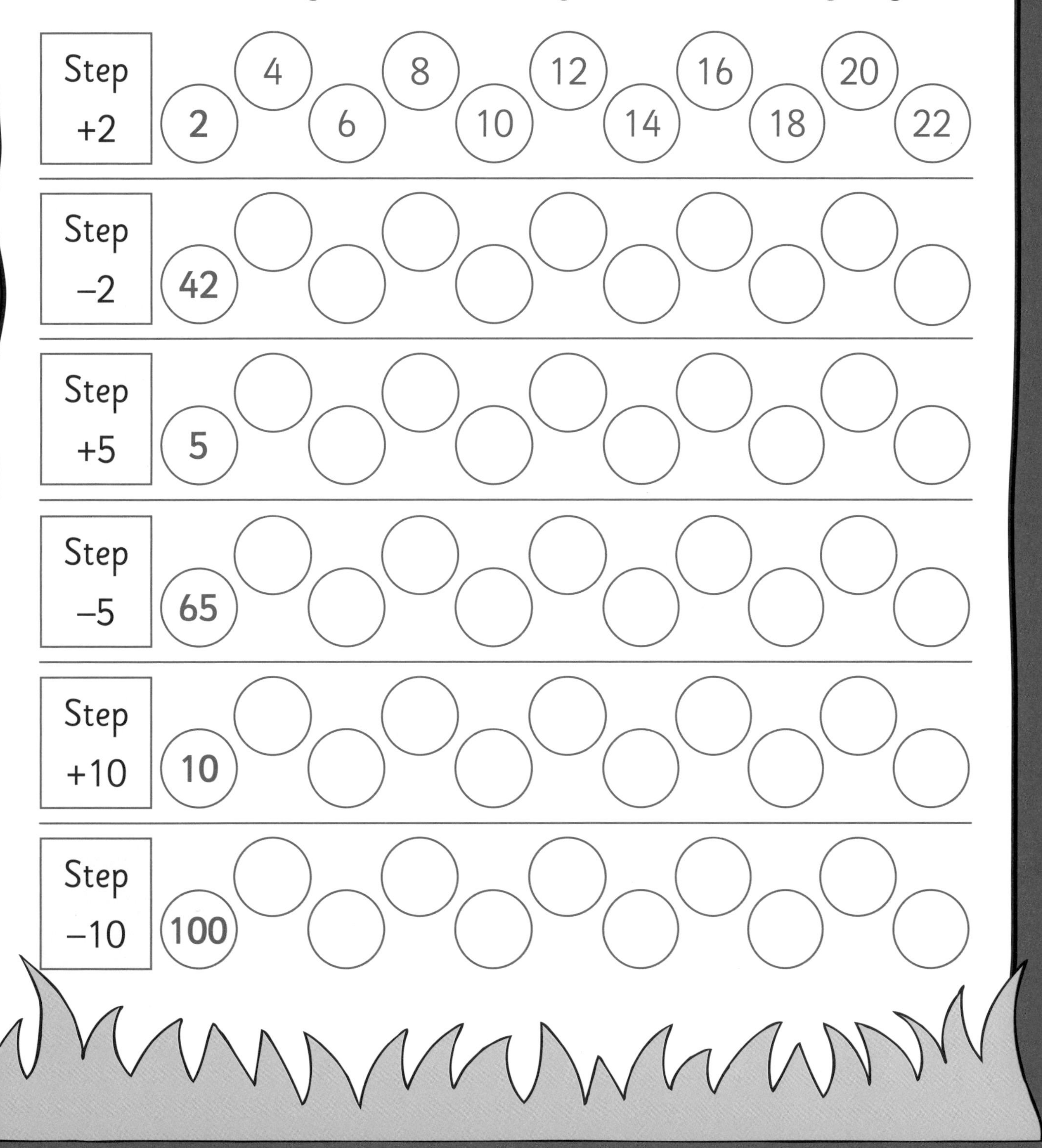

Combining 10s and 1s

2-digit numbers are made up by combining 10s and 1s:
28 = 20 + 8.

Put the 10s and 1s cards together to make 16 new numbers. Record each sum. One has been done for you:

Place value grid

With the number **163**, work out:
How many 100s are in that number?
How many 10s? How many 1s?

100s	10s	1s
1	6	3

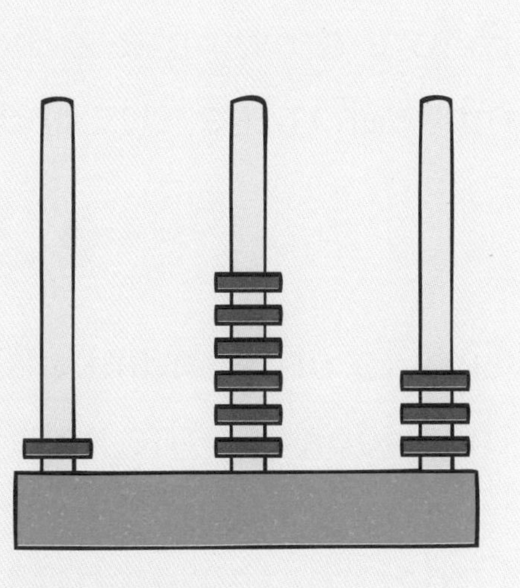

This will help you with additions and subtractions.

Partition these numbers into 100s, 10s and 1s. Write them in the correct column in the table.

	100s	10s	1s
seventy-eight			
forty-seven			
one hundred and twenty-three			
one hundred and four			
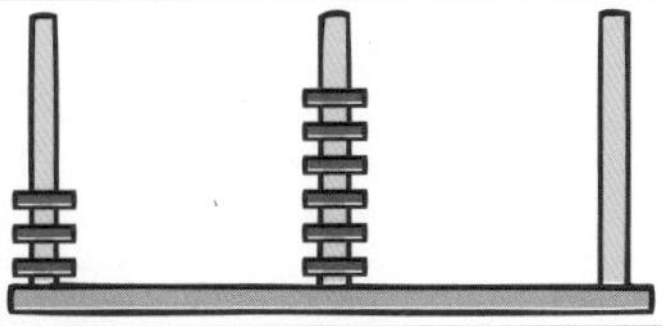			

Ordering and drawing numbers

Before drawing a 2-digit number on an abacus, decide which number is the 10s and which is the 1s:

two 10s → 27 ← seven 1s

Tip: To order numbers, start with the lowest 10s number, and then look for the next lowest 10s number.

Order these numbers from lowest to highest. Write them in the small boxes below.

89 45 57 23 94 69 ~~17~~ 38 70

Draw an abacus picture to match each number.

17

Comparing and ordering numbers

Look at the 10s number to help you order numbers.
For **5**4 and **3**7, 37 has fewer 10s than 54, so is the lower number.
If the 10s numbers are the same, look at the 1s.
For 3**5** and 3**7**, 35 has five 1s, so is lower than 37.

1. Help Charlie arrange these chairs in the correct order – lowest number first.

lowest highest

2. Put these weights in order, starting with the smallest.

31kg 22kg 50kg 43kg 14kg 45kg

3. Put these lengths in order, starting with the longest.

33cm 16cm 41cm 17cm 49cm 20cm

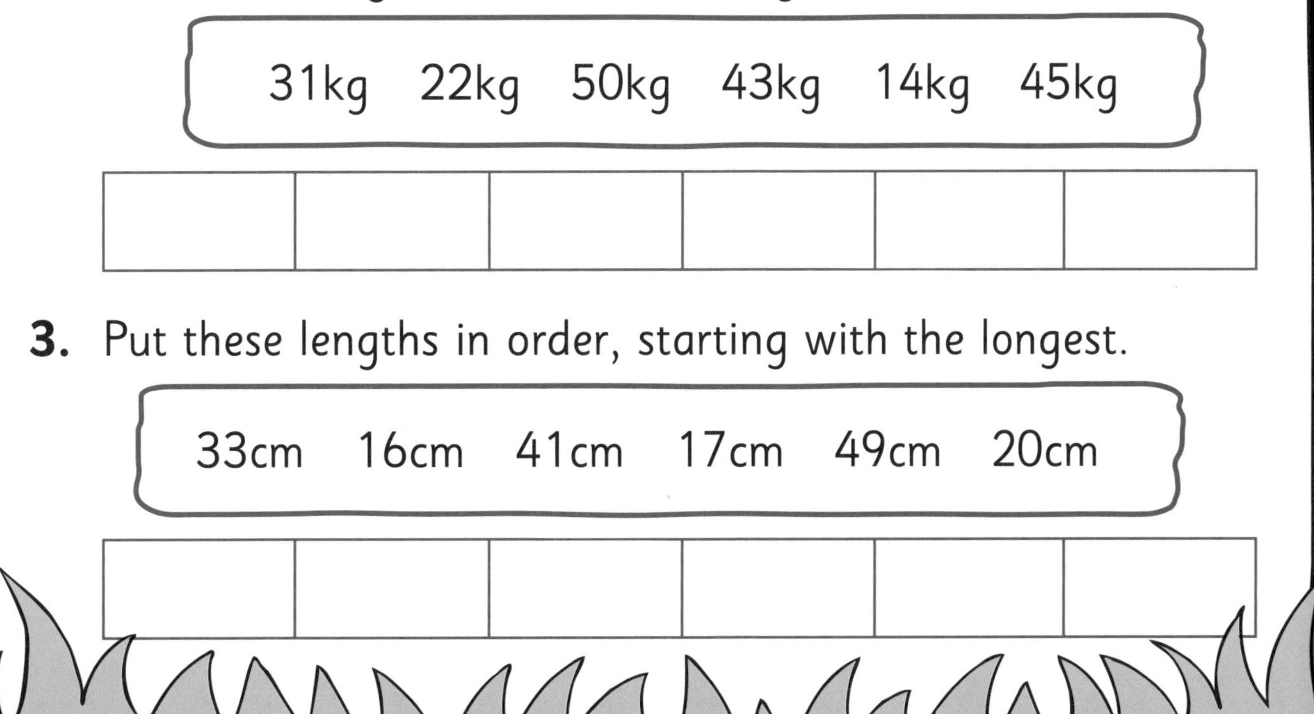

Using <, > and =

< means **less than** 15 < 20.
> means **greater than** 20 > 15.
Tip: The open part of the sign always faces the bigger number.
= means **the same as** or **equals**: 5 = 5.

Fill in the missing sign: <, > or =.

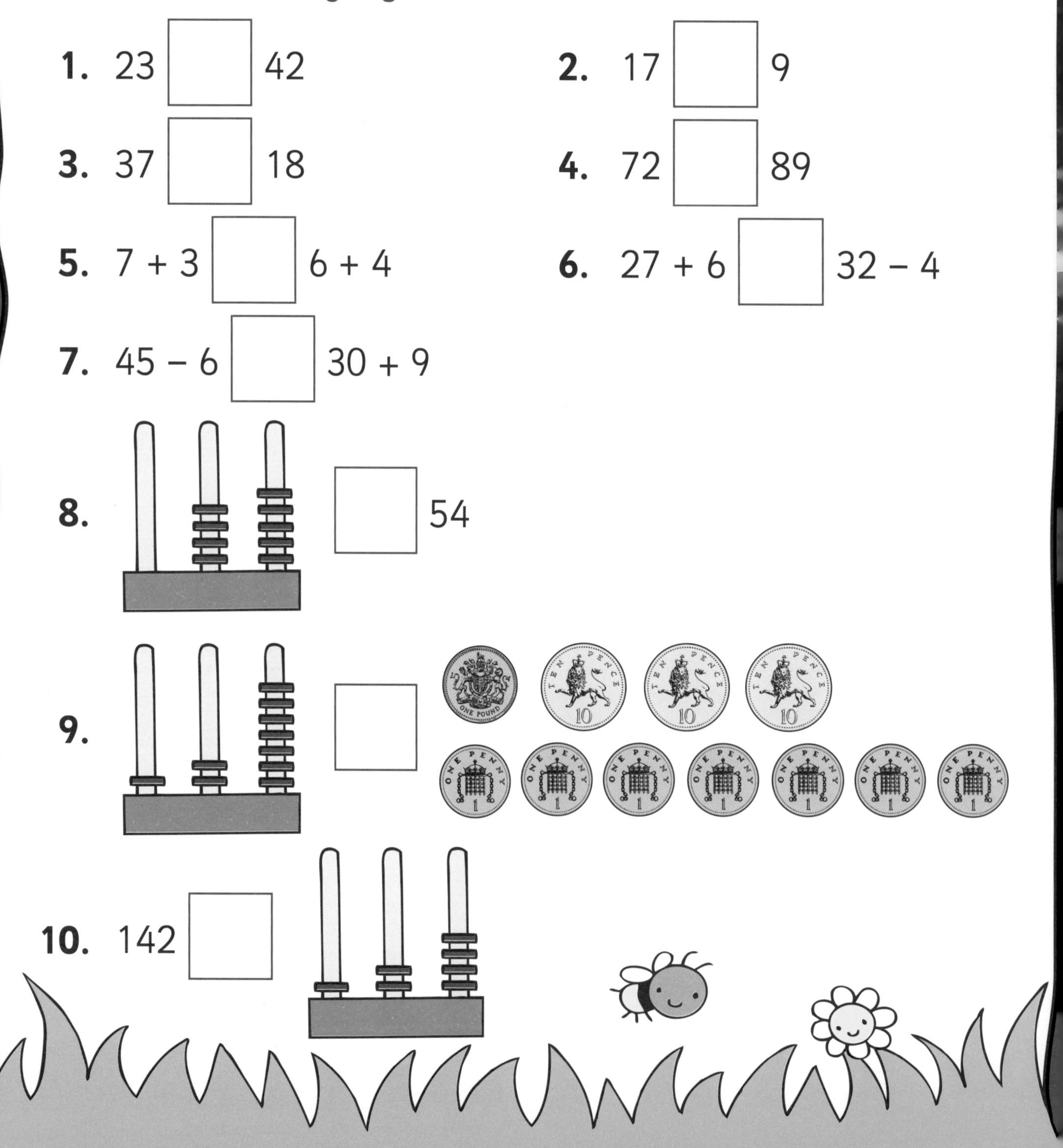

1. 23 ☐ 42

2. 17 ☐ 9

3. 37 ☐ 18

4. 72 ☐ 89

5. 7 + 3 ☐ 6 + 4

6. 27 + 6 ☐ 32 – 4

7. 45 – 6 ☐ 30 + 9

8. ☐ 54

9. ☐

10. 142 ☐

Are these true or false? Tick the correct box.

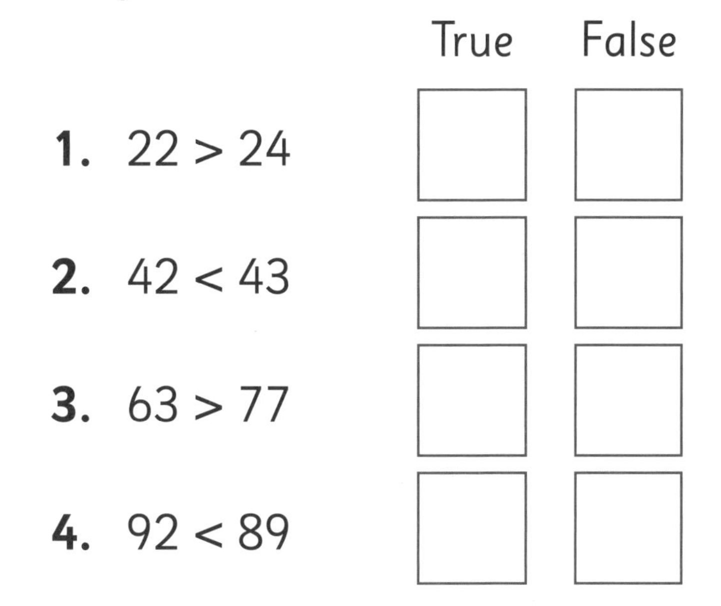

	True	False
1. $22 > 24$		
2. $42 < 43$		
3. $63 > 77$		
4. $92 < 89$		

Write the correct sign: $<$ or $>$.

1. ______

2. ______

3. ______

Estimating numbers on a number line

To estimate, think where halfway would be.
Where would 1 be? Where would 10 be?

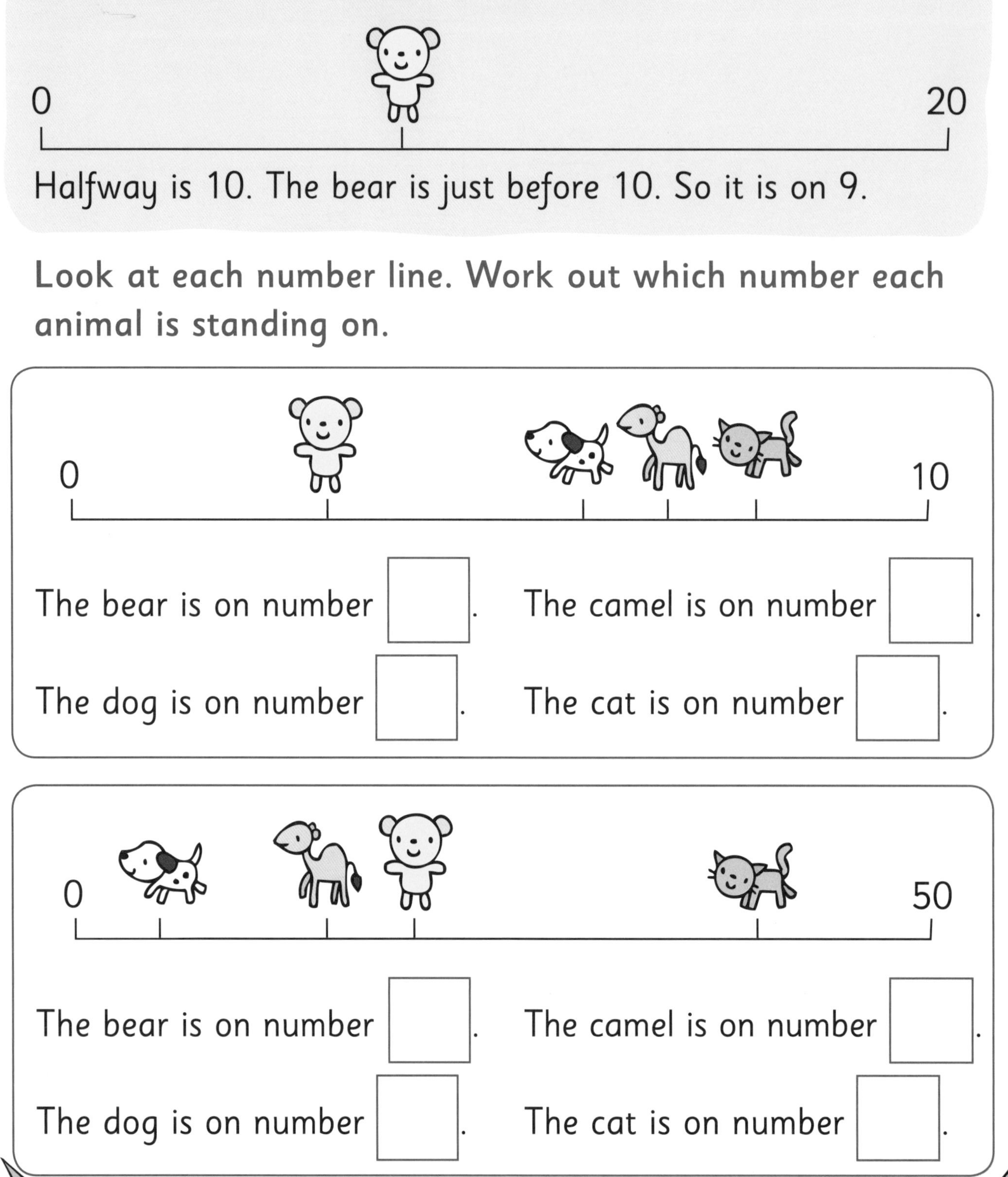

Halfway is 10. The bear is just before 10. So it is on 9.

Look at each number line. Work out which number each animal is standing on.

The bear is on number ☐. The camel is on number ☐.

The dog is on number ☐. The cat is on number ☐.

The bear is on number ☐. The camel is on number ☐.

The dog is on number ☐. The cat is on number ☐.

Great estimate!

To estimate, ask: Is the number between 0 and 10? 10 and 20? 30 and 40? 50 and 100?

Write your estimate and then count in groups to help you.

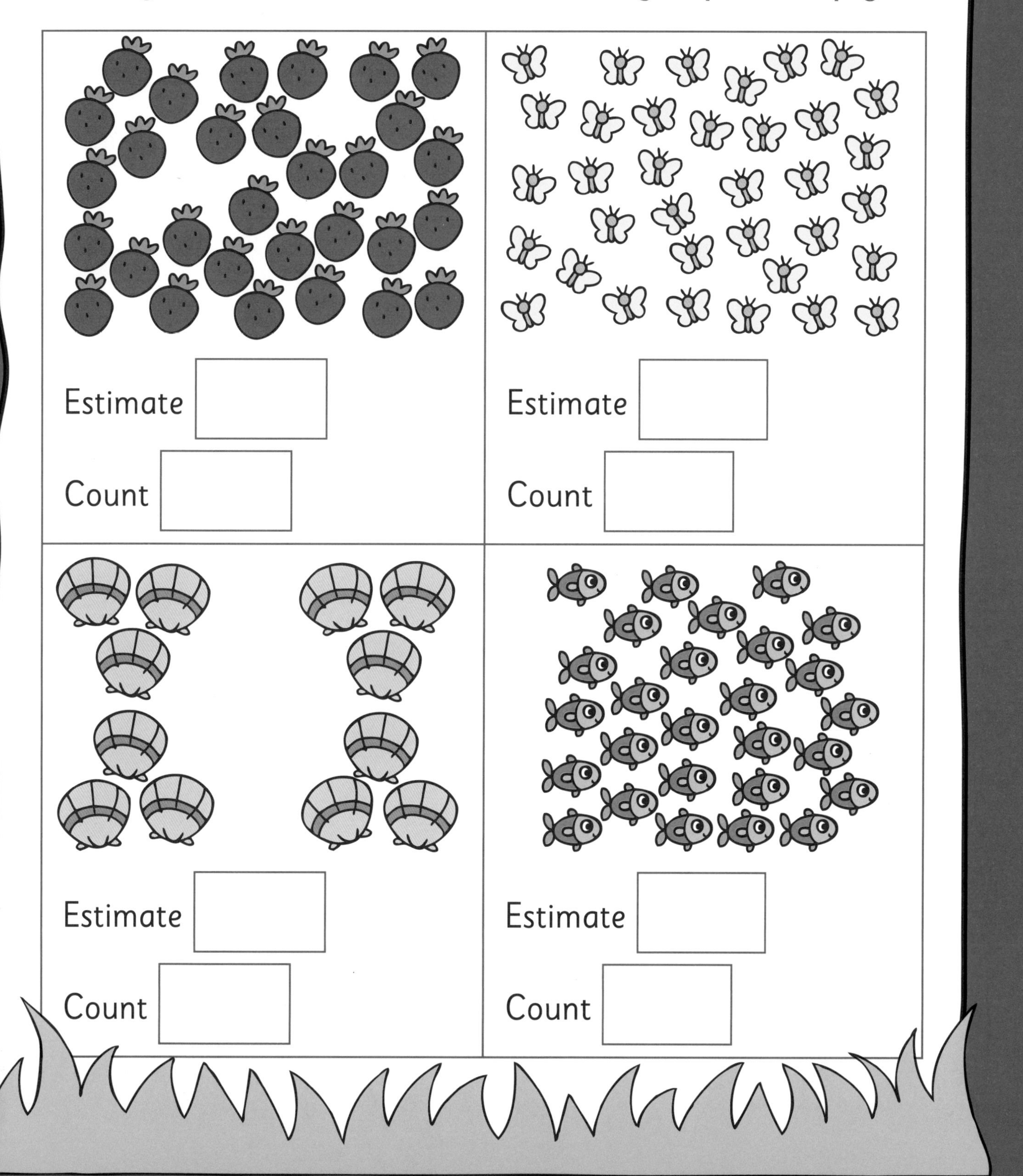

Writing numbers to 100

Practise writing numbers in numerals and in words.
For **34**, put **thirty** and **four** together to make **thirty-four.**
Try making two-digit numbers.

How many new 2-digit numbers can you find, using the five cards below? Write each number, and its name, in the space below. One has been done for you.

2 3 4 7 8

Helpful words

twenty	two
thirty	three
forty	four
seventy	seven
eighty	eight

47, forty-seven	

Place-value problems

For some problems you may have to round your answer up or down.
Sometimes, drawing the items in the problem will help you to solve it. In this problem you could draw boxes and put 10 pencils in each one.

1. Pencils are packed in boxes of 10.
How many boxes will I need for:

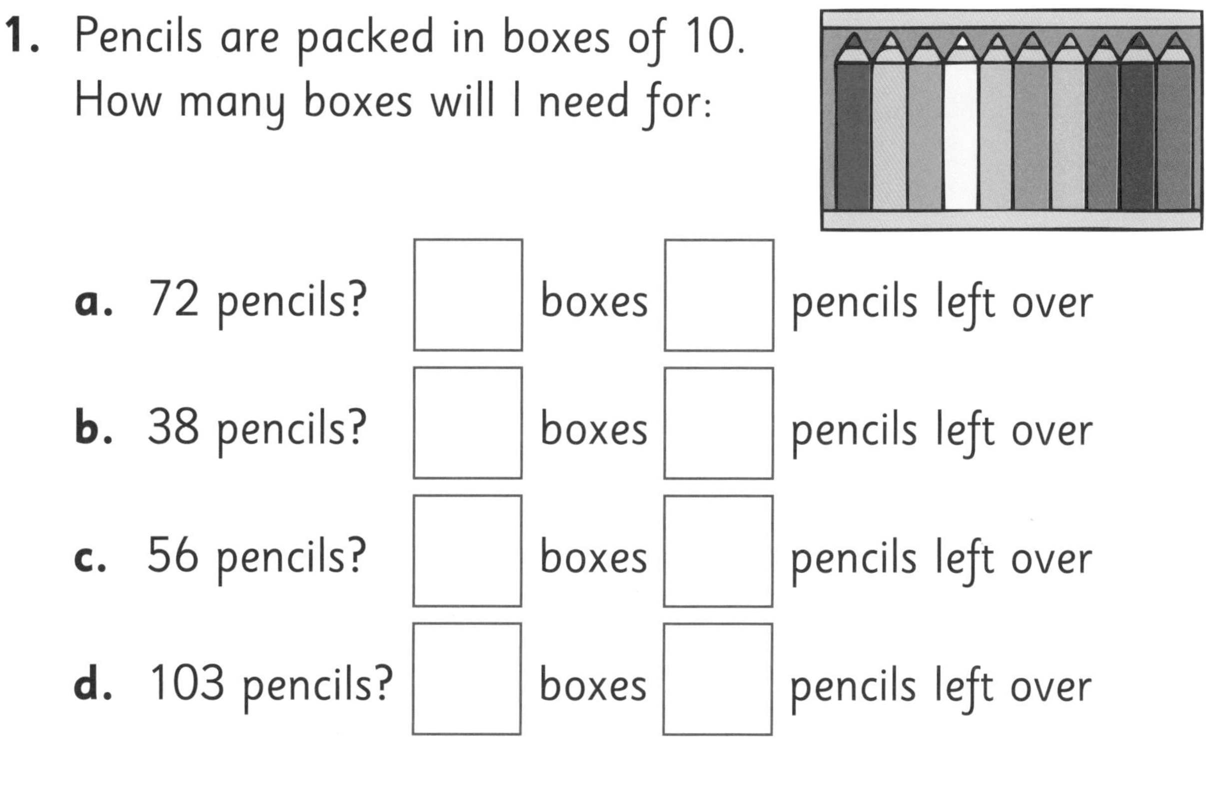

a. 72 pencils? ☐ boxes ☐ pencils left over

b. 38 pencils? ☐ boxes ☐ pencils left over

c. 56 pencils? ☐ boxes ☐ pencils left over

d. 103 pencils? ☐ boxes ☐ pencils left over

2. I have some boxes of pencils and a few left over.
How many pencils are there altogether if:

a. I have 2 boxes and 7 left over? ☐ pencils

b. I have 4 boxes and 3 left over? ☐ pencils

c. I have 9 boxes and 1 left over? ☐ pencils

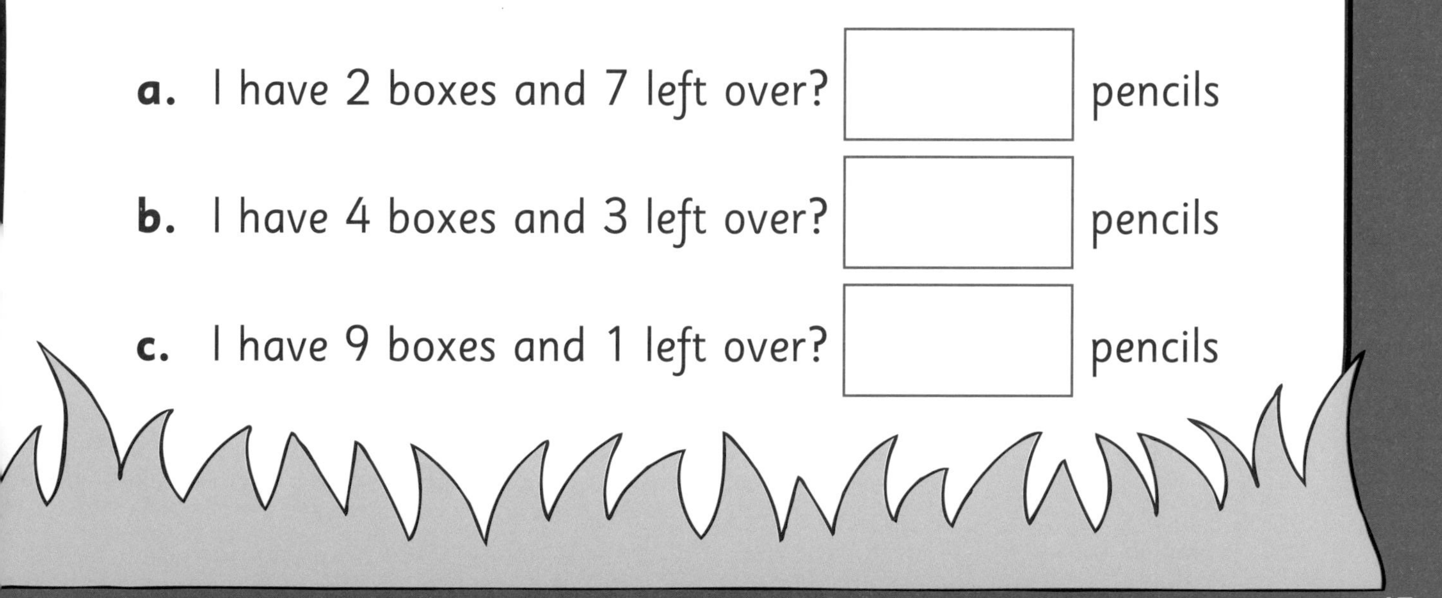

Numbers to 20

Practise adding numbers to 10, as these will help you work out addition to 20.
If you know 1 + 9 = 10, it will help you remember that 1**1 + 9** = 20.
The 1s are the same. Use cubes to help you work out the bonds to 20.

You have two darts to throw at the target.
You must score 20.

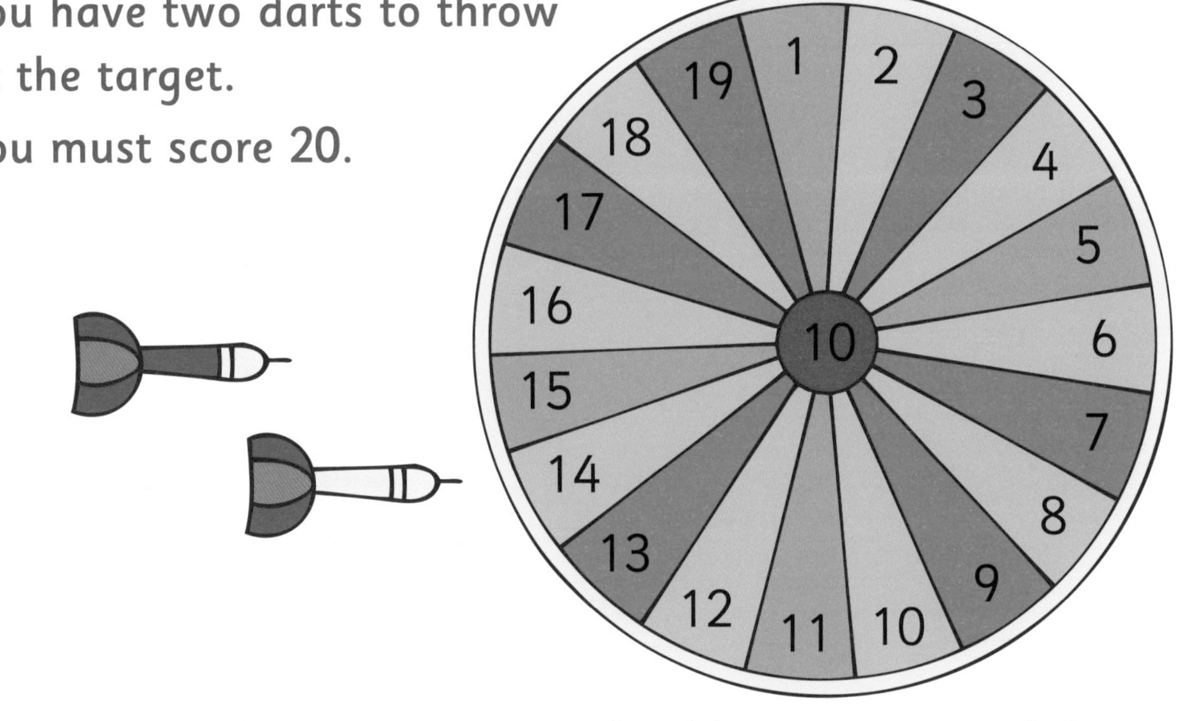

Write the different ways to make 20 using pairs of these numbers.

____

____

____

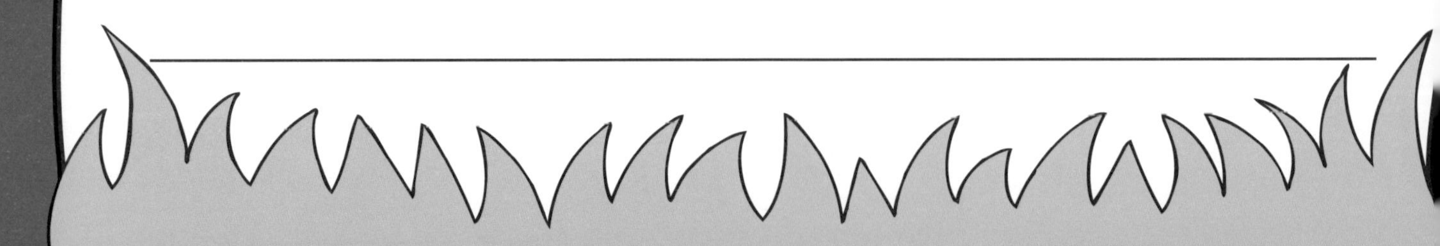

Make 20!

Joe has 20 marbles. He puts some in each of his two pockets.

How many different ways can he do this?

Use the table below to record your work.

Pocket 1	Pocket 2

Numbers to 100

Practise adding numbers to 10.
This will help you add to 100.
Use blocks or cubes to help you
You know that 2 + 8 = 10, so:
20 + 80 = 100.

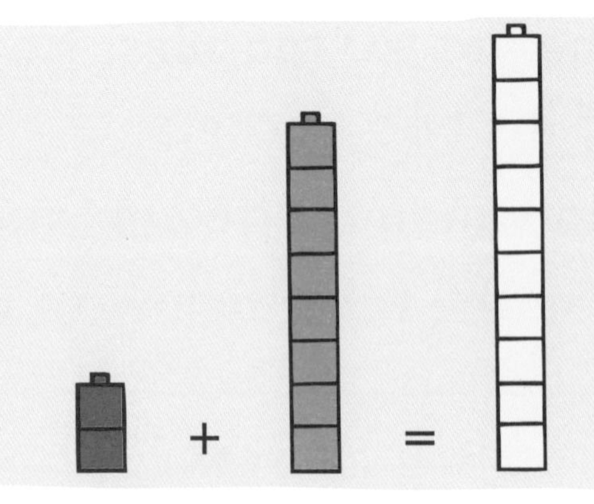

You have two darts to throw at the target.
You must score 100.

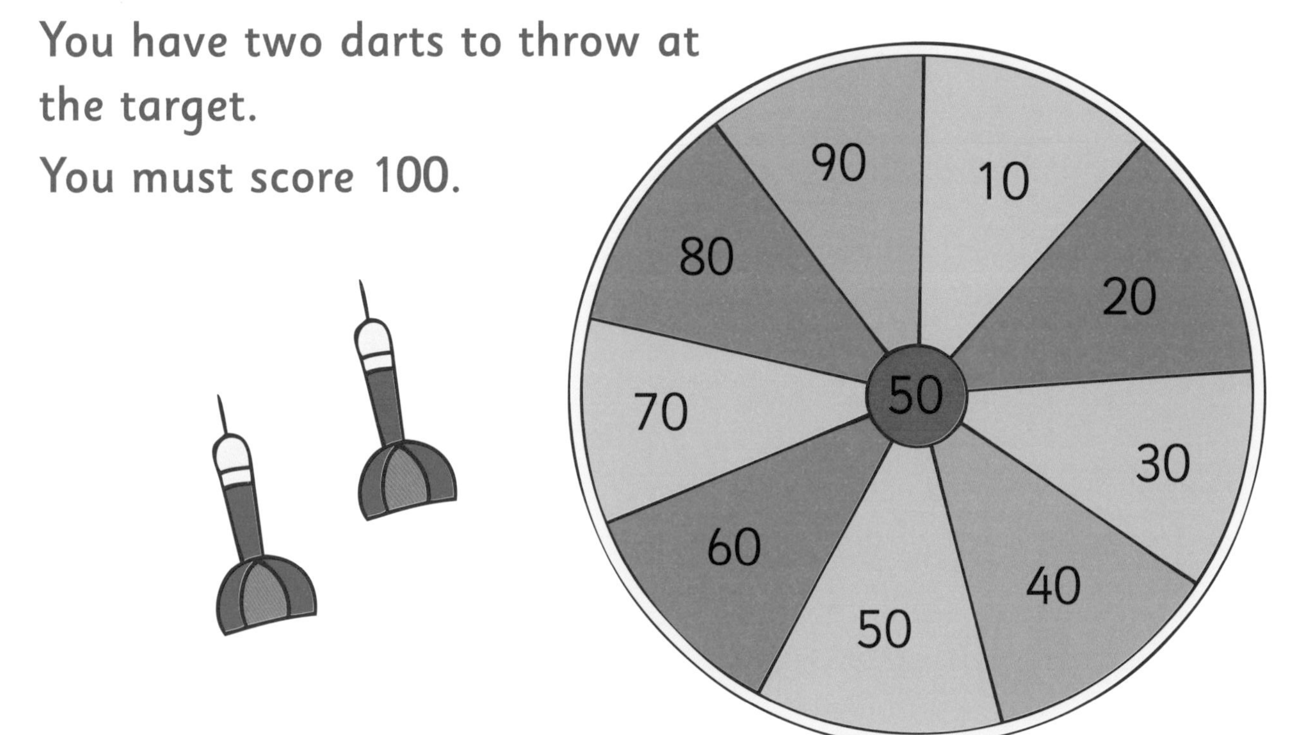

Write the different ways to make 100 using pairs of these numbers.

____

____

____

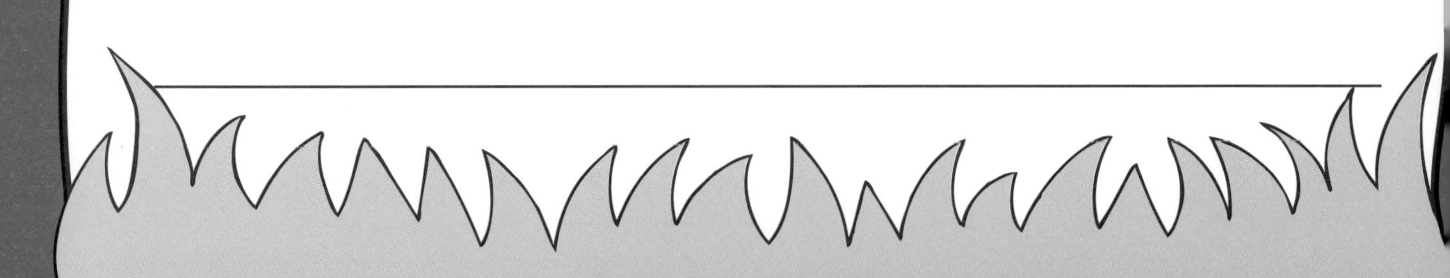

Perfect Peter has found seven ways to make 100 using any two numbers. He has challenged you to find more.

- Here is one to start you off: 60 + 40 = 100.
- And here is another one: 1 + 99 = 100.

1. How many more can you find?

2. Do you think you found them all?

Addition and subtraction

Knowing an addition fact can help you work out a subtraction fact with the same numbers.
If you know that 5 + 4 = 9, you can use it to work out that 9 – 5 = 4.

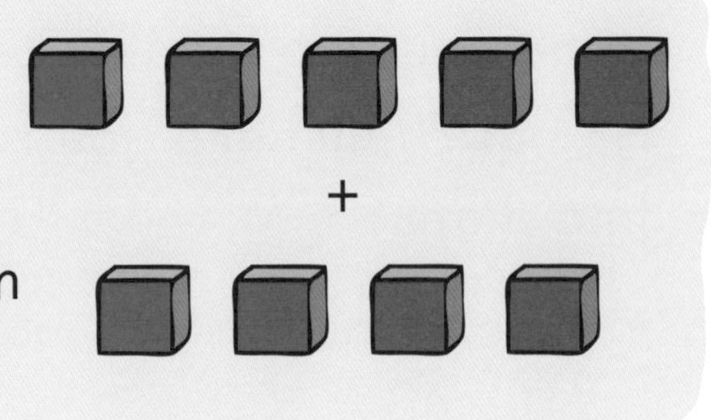

1. Fill in the missing amounts in these two sets.

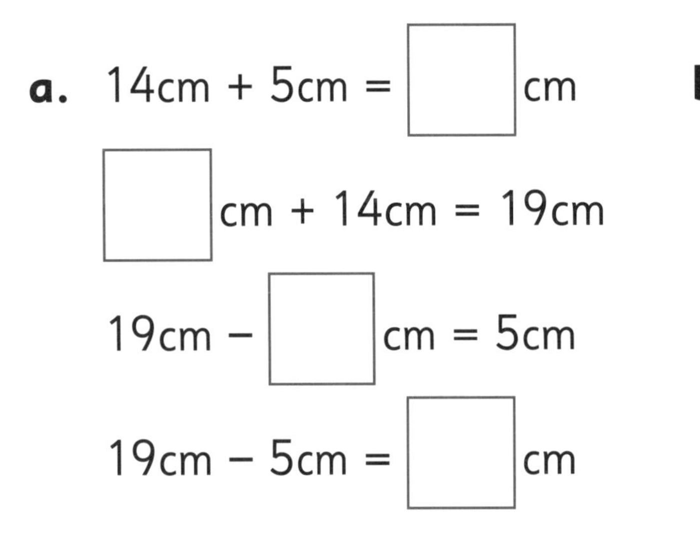

a. 14cm + 5cm = ☐ cm

☐ cm + 14cm = 19cm

19cm – ☐ cm = 5cm

19cm – 5cm = ☐ cm

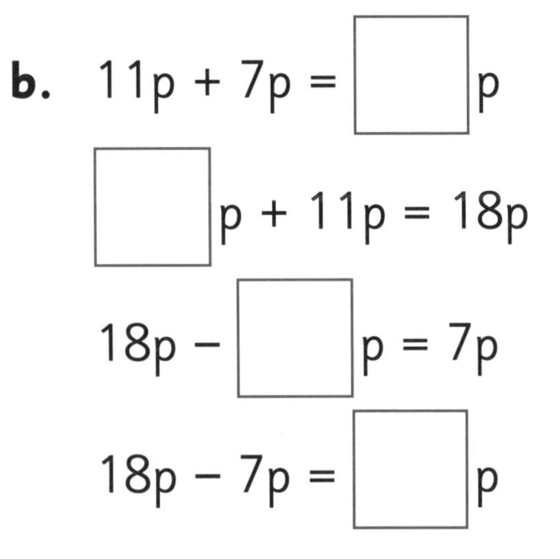

b. 11p + 7p = ☐ p

☐ p + 11p = 18p

18p – ☐ p = 7p

18p – 7p = ☐ p

2. Now answer these questions:

a. 17m + 12m = ☐ m

☐ m + 17m = 29m

29m – ☐ m = 17m

29m – 17m = ☐ m

b. 30g + 50g = ☐ g

☐ g + 30g = 80g

80g – ☐ g = 50g

80g – 50g = ☐ g

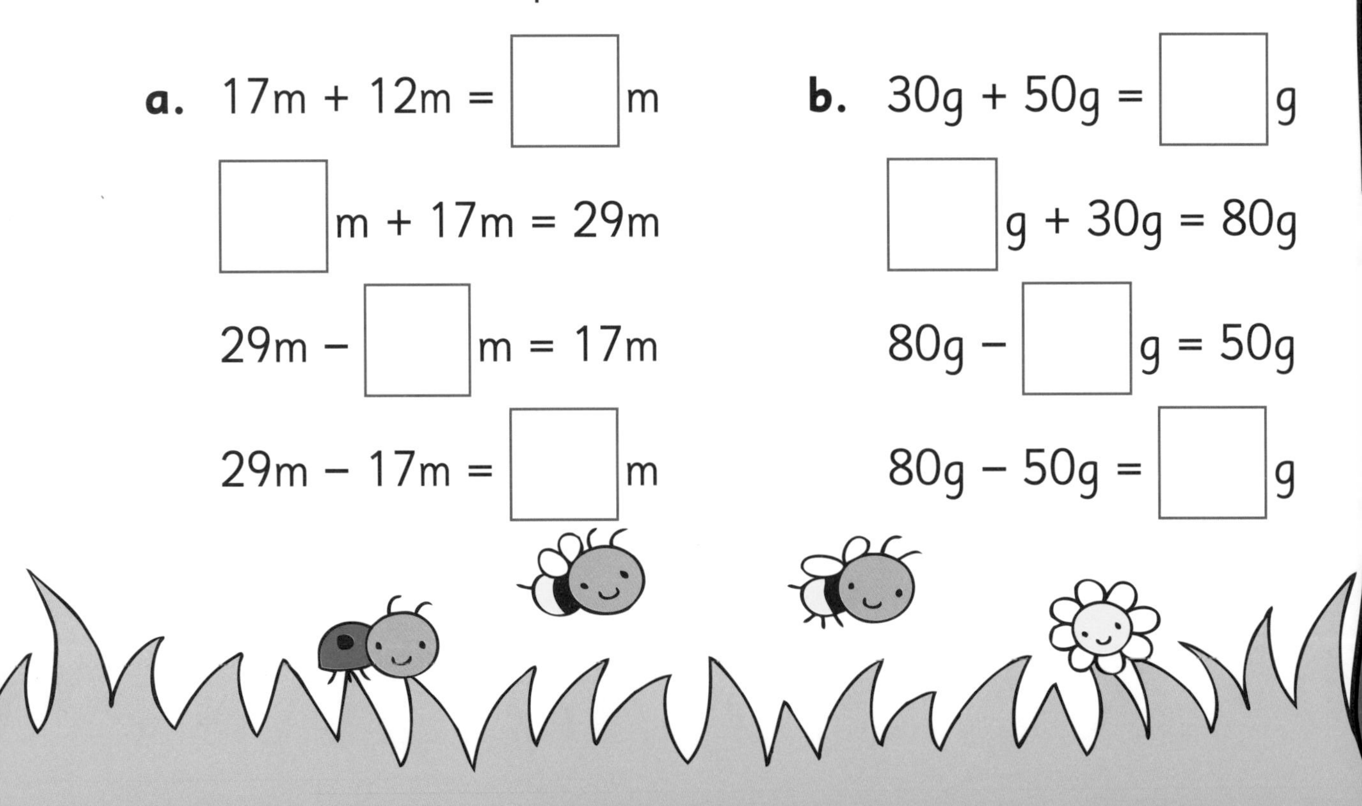

Inverse match

Inverse means the **opposite**. Subtraction is the **inverse** (the opposite) of addition.
Look at the addition 4 + 3 = 7. The **inverse** is 7 – 3 = 4.
Tip: The subtraction always starts with the total from the addition.

Draw a line to match each addition to its inverse subtraction.

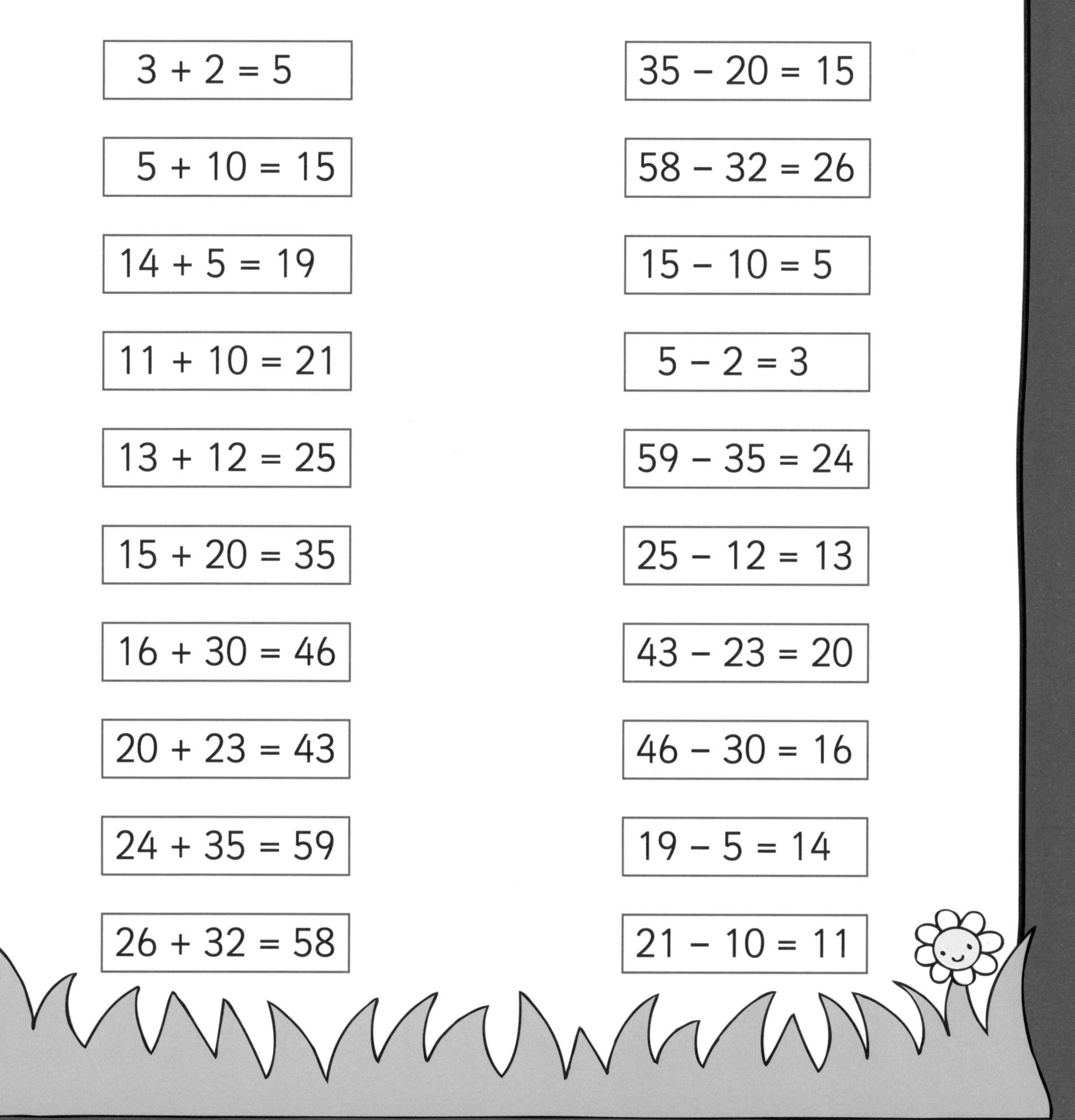

Adding order

You can add numbers in any order:
so 5 + 3 = 8, but 3 + 5 = 8 as well.
It is easier to start with the larger number. Put the larger number in your head and count on the smaller number.

1. Rewrite with the larger number first. Then find the totals.

a. 5 + 13 = 13 + 5 = 18

b. 8 + 11 = ________ = ____

c. 3 + 16 = ________ = ____

d. 6 + 14 = ________ = ____

e. 5 + 12 = ________ = ____

f. 3 + 17 = ________ = ____

2. Use each number to make six sums. Put the larger number first each time. Find all the answers.

____ + ____ = ____ 11 41 23 32 ____ + ____ = ____

____ + ____ = ____ 21 34 43 31 ____ + ____ = ____

____ + ____ = ____ 44 13 42 22 ____ + ____ = ____

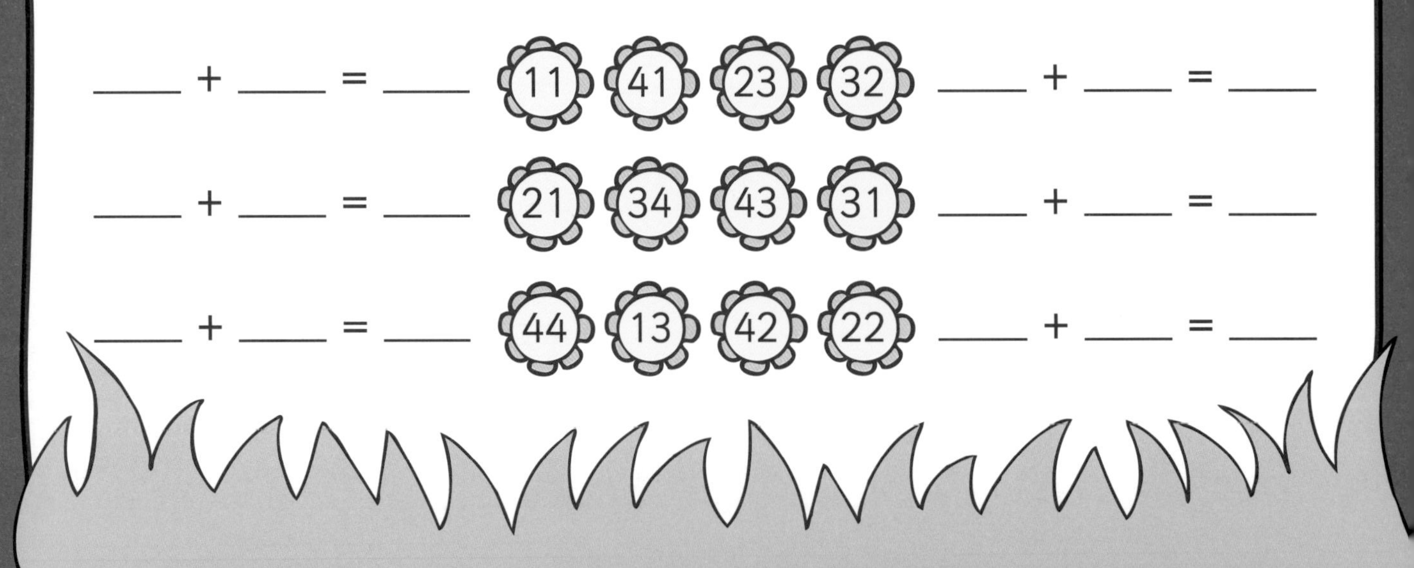

Totals to 10

Adding three numbers is easier if you can find two numbers that total 10, for example, to add 8, 6, and 4: start by adding 6 and 4 (10) and then add 8. 10 + 8 = 18.

Choose three numbers to add together.

Make sure that two of them total 10. Next, add the third number.

2 3 4 6 7 8 12 13 14 16 17 18

Numbers chosen	Numbers totalling 10	Addition

Addition problems

Read the problem. Try different methods to solve them. Write down each correct addition sentence.

1. Unlucky Ducky is trying to make the number 13 with these cards. How many different ways could she do it, using number 6 as one of the cards each time?

____

____

____

2. How many ways can you score 12 by rolling three dice?

____

____

____

Party subtraction problems

Read each problem. Write a subtraction sentence for each one. Work out the answer.

Tip: Each sentence starts with the larger number, 20.

On Saturday, Sam had a birthday party.

1. 20 friends came to his party. 3 were girls. How many were boys?

2. He blew up 20 balloons. 12 were blue. The rest were yellow. How many balloons were yellow?

3. He received 20 presents. 5 were in bags. The rest were in boxes. How many presents were in boxes?

4. He made 20 hats. 14 were stripy. The rest were spotty. How many were spotty?

5. He made 20 sandwiches. 11 were jam. The rest were cheese. How many were cheese?

6. He had 20 candles on his cake. 7 were pink. The rest were orange. How many were orange?

Repeated addition and subtraction

2 × 3 is the same as 2 + 2 + 2, or 3 lots of 2

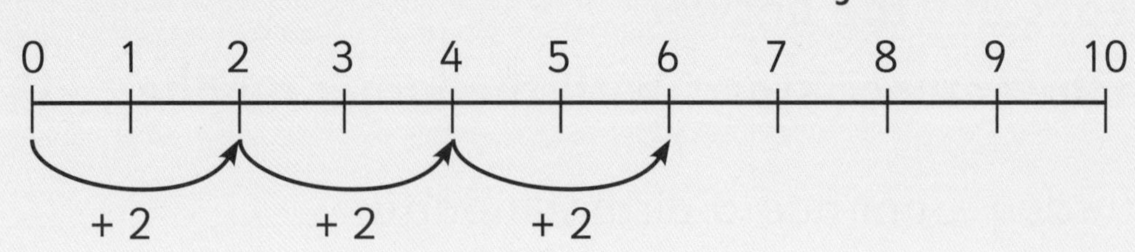

Complete the number lines by drawing jumps along the lines to show the multiplication in each box.

Write your calculation and the answer underneath each number line.

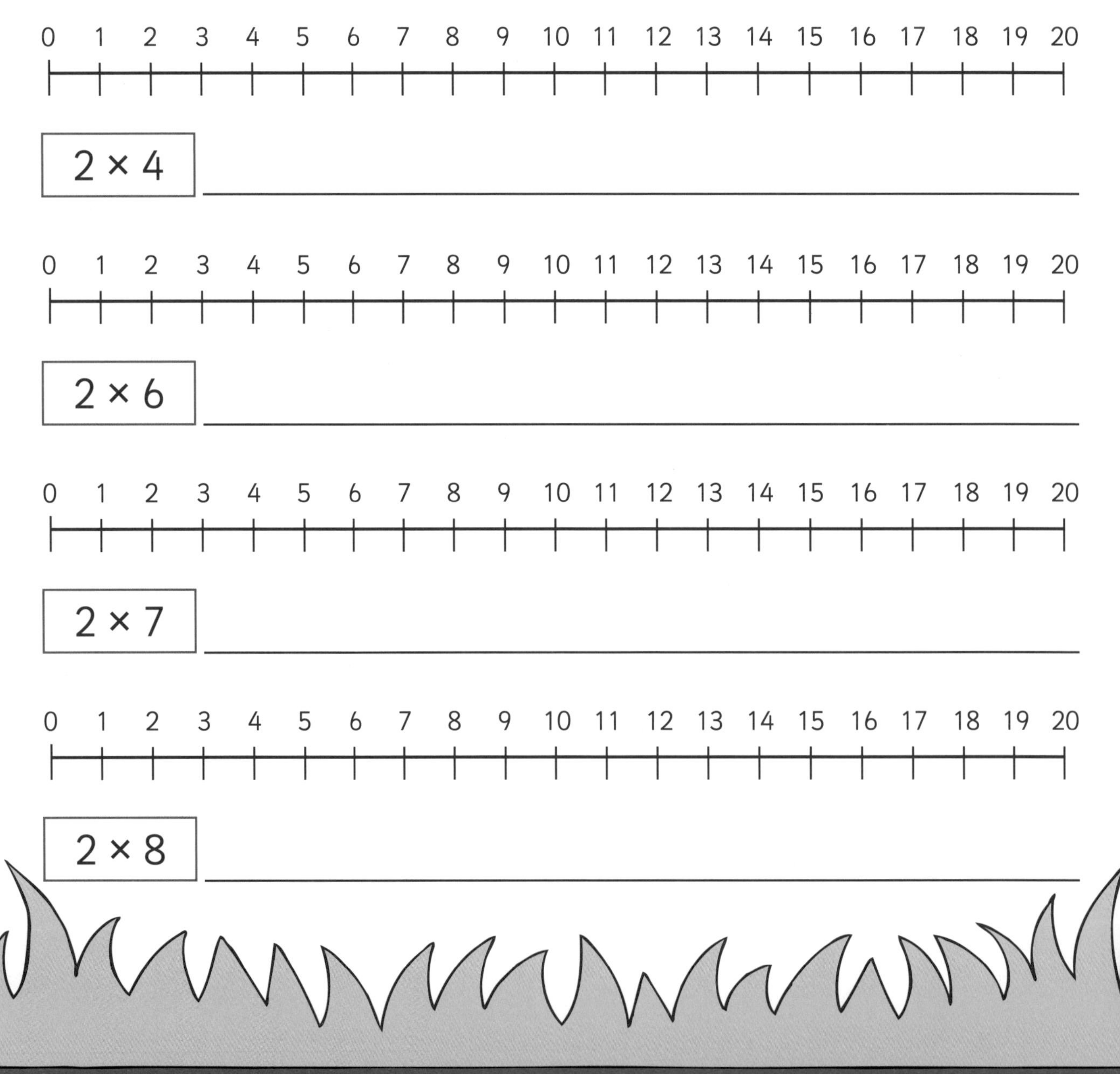

Repeated subtraction can be used to show division.

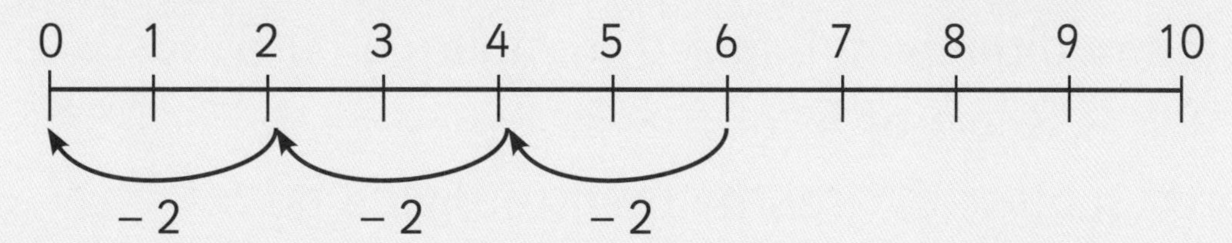

Three lots of 2 have been subtracted so 6 ÷ 2 = 3

Complete the number lines by drawing jumps along the lines to show the division in each box.

Write your calculation and the answer underneath each number line.

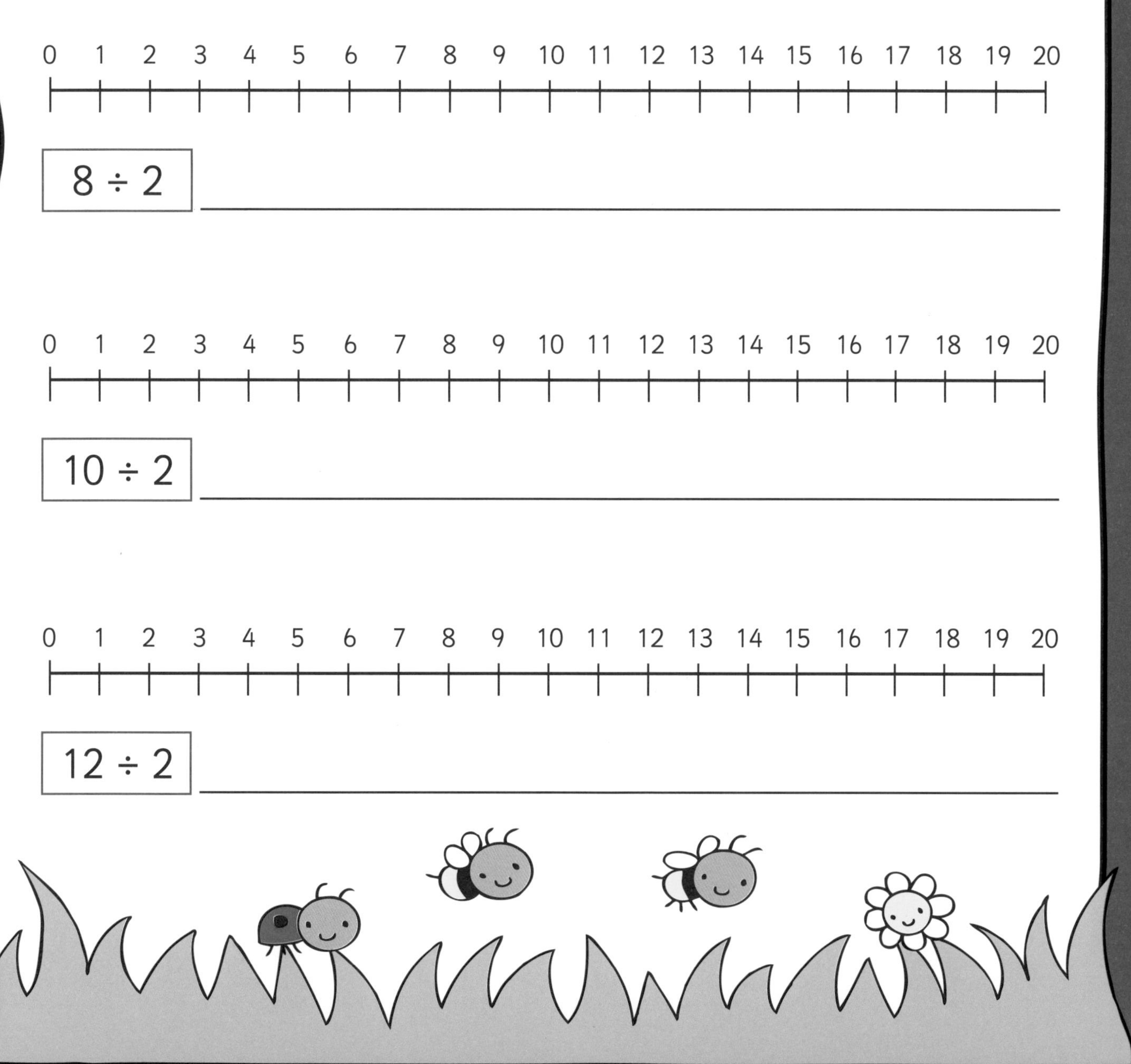

Repeated addition and subtraction (2)

Repeated addition can be used to multiply by 5, so:
5 + 5 + 5 is 3 lots of 5, or 5 × 3
Repeated subtraction can be used to divide by 5.

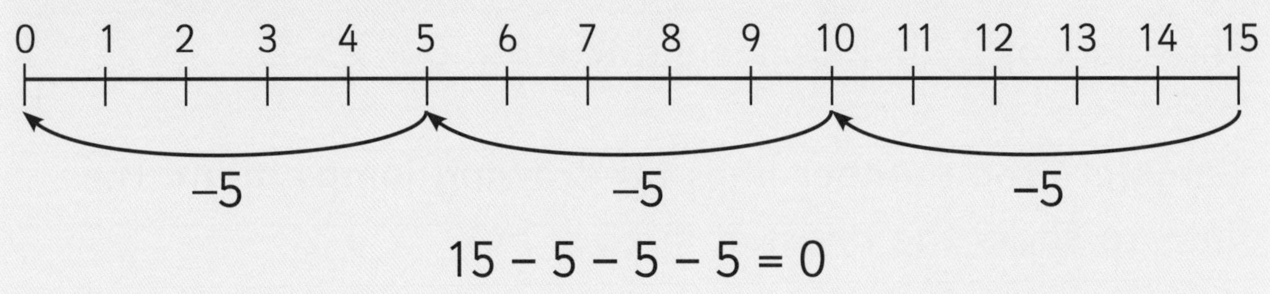

15 – 5 – 5 – 5 = 0

Complete the number lines by drawing jumps along the lines to show the multiplication or division in each box. Write your calculation and the answer underneath each number line.

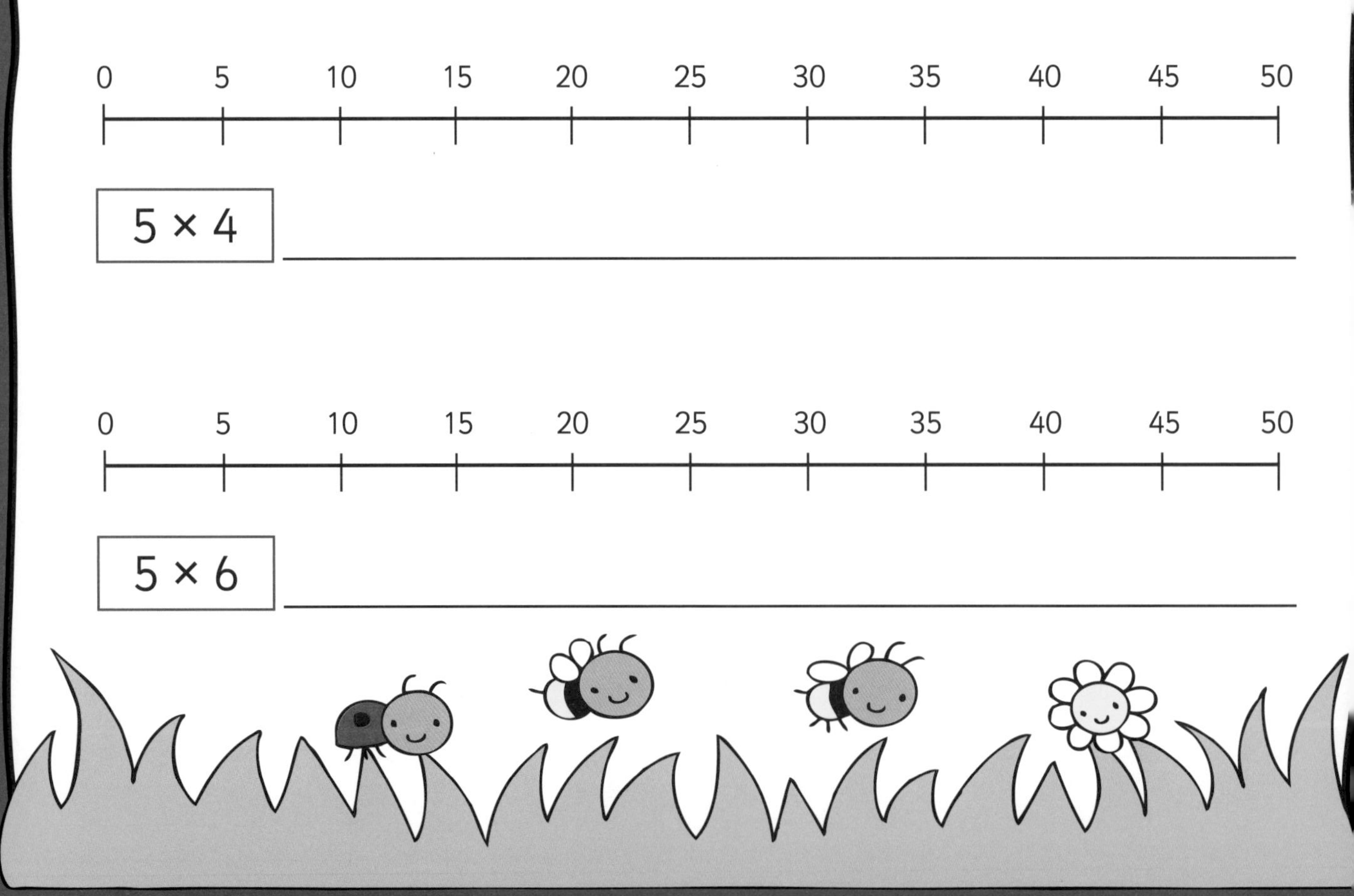

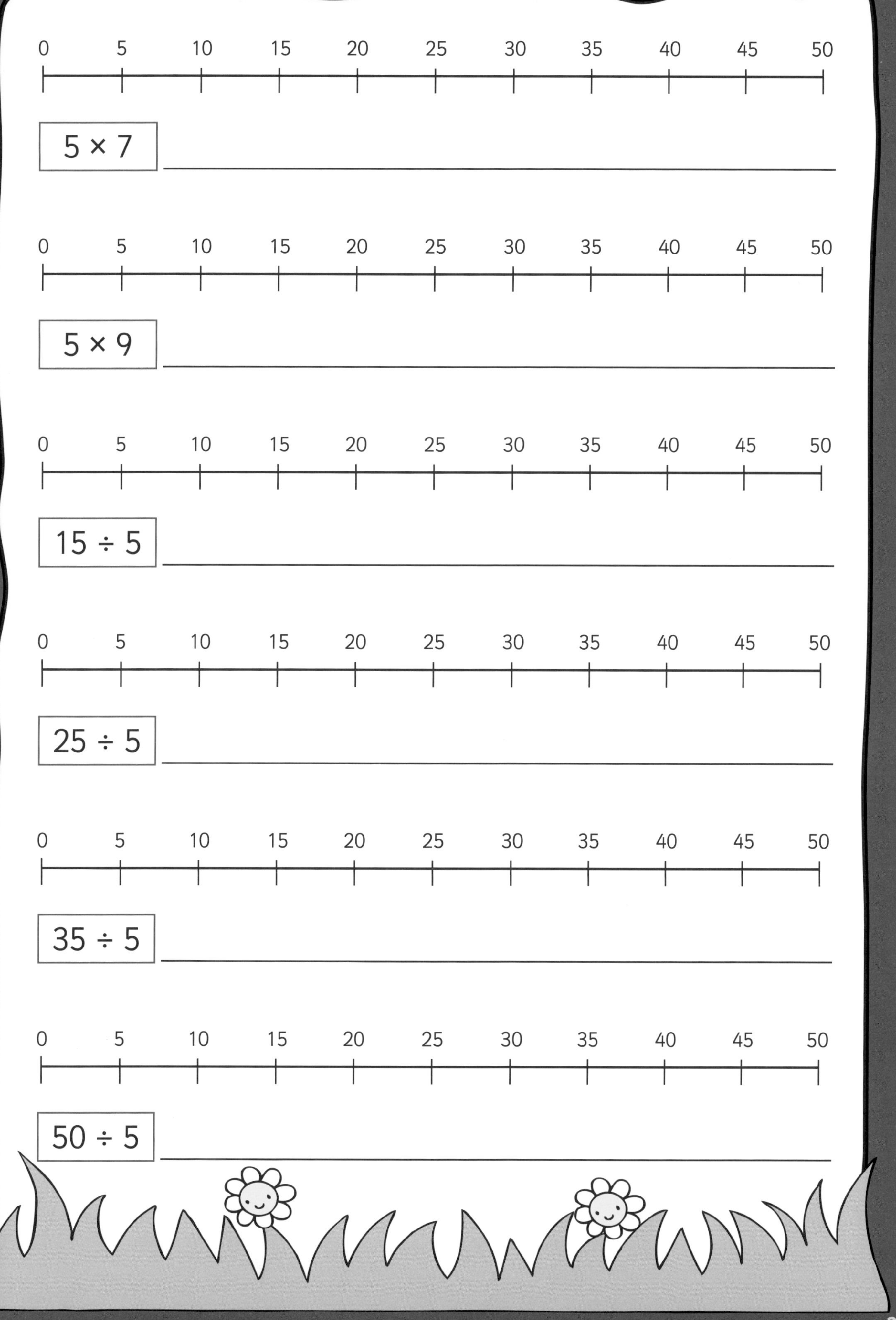
0 5 10 15 20 25 30 35 40 45 50
5 × 7
0 5 10 15 20 25 30 35 40 45 50
5 × 9
0 5 10 15 20 25 30 35 40 45 50
15 ÷ 5
0 5 10 15 20 25 30 35 40 45 50
25 ÷ 5
0 5 10 15 20 25 30 35 40 45 50
35 ÷ 5
0 5 10 15 20 25 30 35 40 45 50
50 ÷ 5

Face the facts

Practise the 2-, 5- and 10-times tables to become quicker at working out number facts in your head.

1. Complete the multiplication grid.

×	2	5	10
2			
4			
1			
5			

2. Complete the multiplication grid.

×	2	5	10
7			
6			
3			
8			

Monster multiplication

Read each problem. Think how many equal groups there are:

3 + 3 + 3 or 3 × 3.

There are nine eyes altogether.

Write a multiplication number sentence for each group of monsters.

5 monsters with 2 eyes each
2 monsters with 7 eyes each
10 monsters with 3 eyes each
5 monsters with 4 eyes each
6 monsters with 10 eyes each
10 monsters with 5 eyes each
5 monsters with 8 eyes each

Multiplication order

3×2 is the same as $2 \times 3 = 6$.

Knowing one multiplication fact helps us to know another one. You can multiply numbers in **any** order and the answer is the same.

1. Below each multiplication fact, write another which gives the same answer. The first one has been done for you.

a. $3 \times 2 = 6$

$2 \times 3 = 6$

b. $2 \times 1 = 2$

____

c. $4 \times 2 = 8$

____

d. $2 \times 5 = 10$

____

e. $5 \times 3 = 15$

____

f. $5 \times 7 = 35$

____

g. $2 \times 7 = 14$

____

h. $9 \times 5 = 45$

____

i. $2 \times 9 = 18$

____

2. Solve the problem.

Five 2p coins have the same value as ____________ coins.

Odd and even multiples

Even numbers always end with 2, 4, 6, 8 or 0 – they are always **multiples of 2**. So 34 is an even number, because it ends in a 4. Numbers that end in 1, 3, 5, 7 or 9 are **odd** numbers.
Some multiples of 5 are odd numbers and some are even.

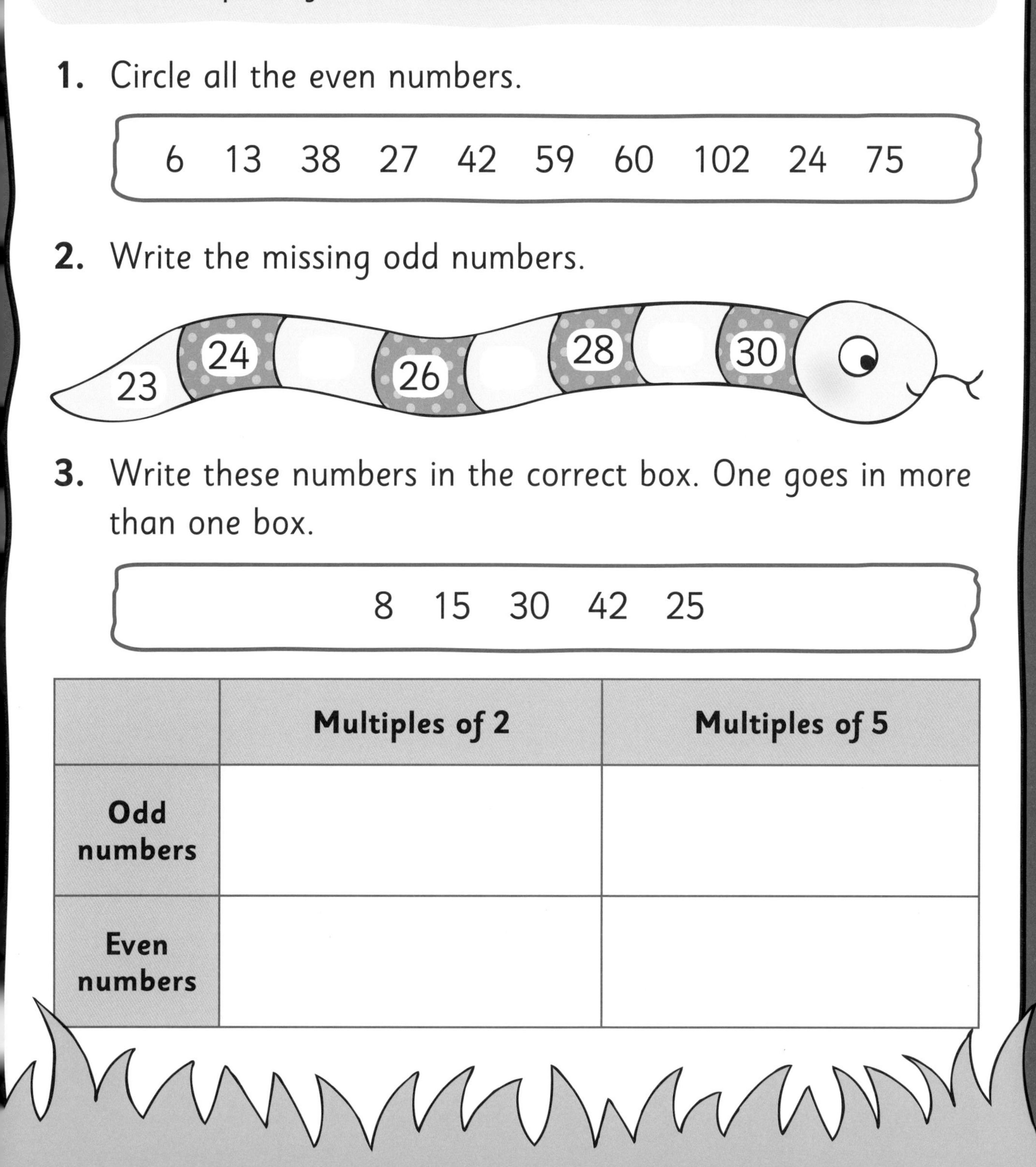

1. Circle all the even numbers.

6 13 38 27 42 59 60 102 24 75

2. Write the missing odd numbers.

3. Write these numbers in the correct box. One goes in more than one box.

8 15 30 42 25

	Multiples of 2	Multiples of 5
Odd numbers		
Even numbers		

Fraction wall

A fraction is a part of a whole, for example $\frac{1}{2}$
A fraction wall shows us how many of each fraction = 1 whole, $\frac{1}{2} + \frac{1}{2} = 1$ whole $\frac{2}{2}$ also = 1 whole

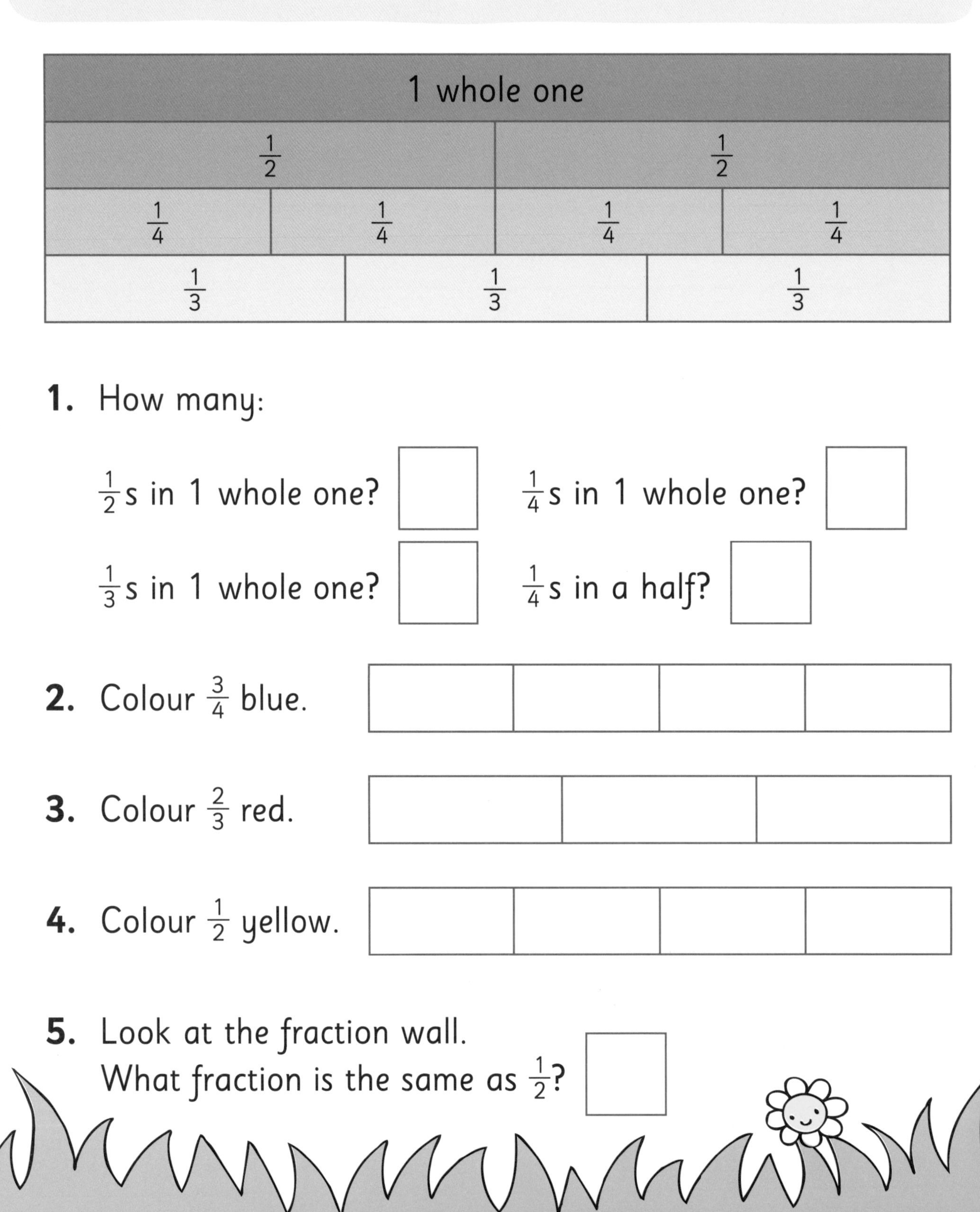

1 whole one					
$\frac{1}{2}$			$\frac{1}{2}$		
$\frac{1}{4}$	$\frac{1}{4}$		$\frac{1}{4}$	$\frac{1}{4}$	
$\frac{1}{3}$		$\frac{1}{3}$		$\frac{1}{3}$	

1. How many:

$\frac{1}{2}$s in 1 whole one? ☐ $\frac{1}{4}$s in 1 whole one? ☐

$\frac{1}{3}$s in 1 whole one? ☐ $\frac{1}{4}$s in a half? ☐

2. Colour $\frac{3}{4}$ blue.

3. Colour $\frac{2}{3}$ red.

4. Colour $\frac{1}{2}$ yellow.

5. Look at the fraction wall.
What fraction is the same as $\frac{1}{2}$? ☐

Equivalent fractions

Remember: $\frac{4}{4}$ is the same as $\frac{1}{4} + \frac{1}{4} + \frac{1}{4} + \frac{1}{4}$
$\frac{4}{4}$ is the same as 1 whole one

1. For each shape, match the shaded area to the corresponding fraction.

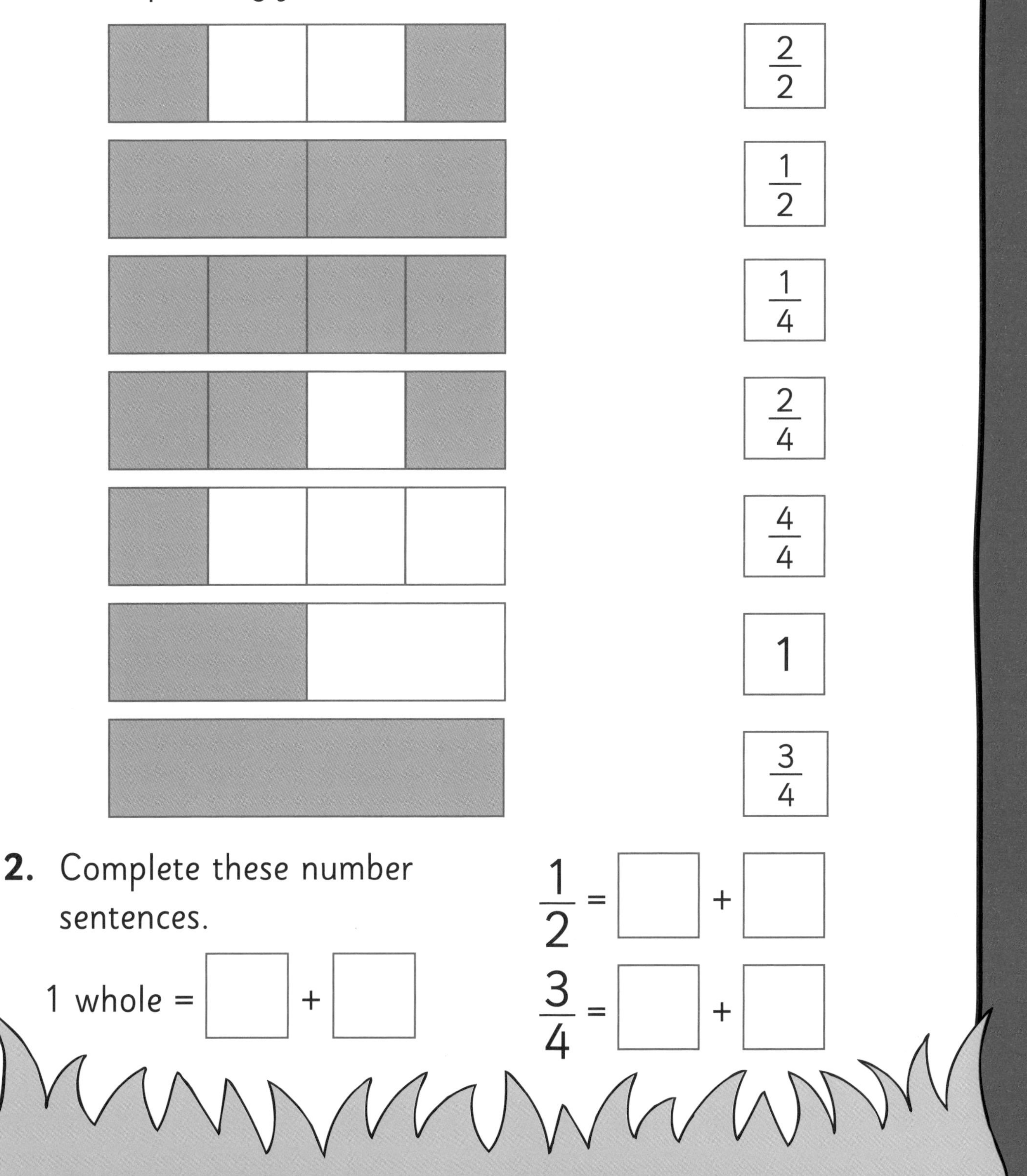

2. Complete these number sentences.

$\frac{1}{2}$ = ☐ + ☐

1 whole = ☐ + ☐

$\frac{3}{4}$ = ☐ + ☐

Three-quarters

To find $\frac{3}{4}$ of 8: count out the number of objects (8) and then split into 4 equal groups.
Each group will be $\frac{1}{4}$ of 8
3 groups = $\frac{3}{4}$ (6)

1. Colour $\frac{3}{4}$ of each shape.

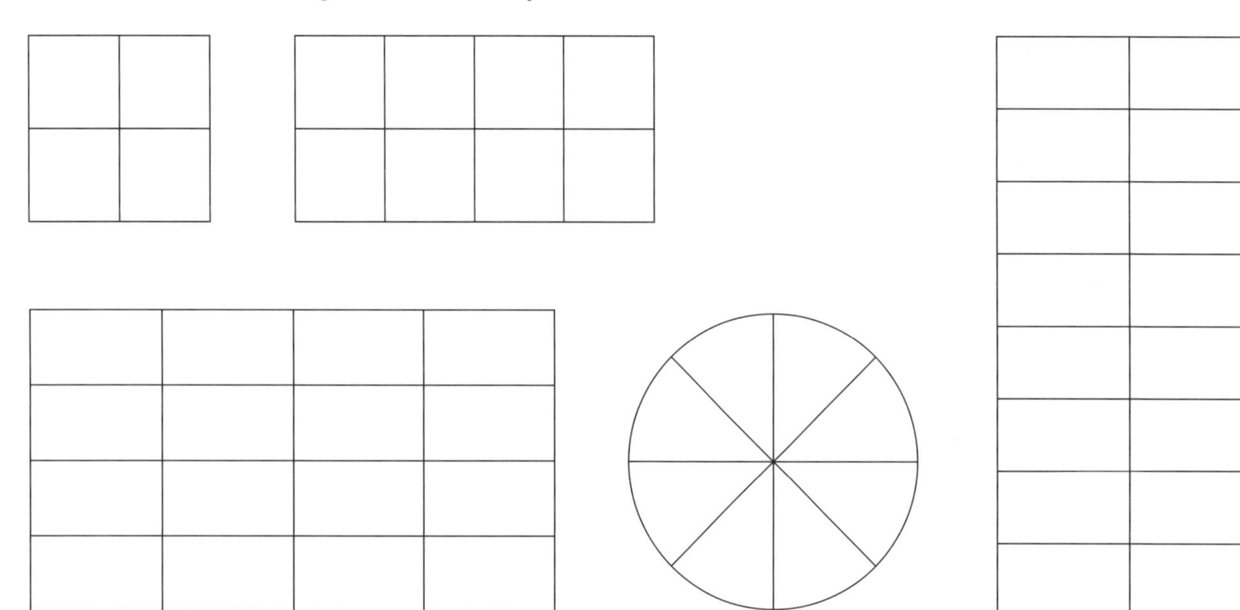

2. Draw a circle around $\frac{3}{4}$ of these groups of objects.

Fractions of objects

Amount	$\frac{1}{2}$	$\frac{1}{4}$	$\frac{3}{4}$
8	4	2	6
12	6	3	9
15	No	No	No

Drop a handful of cubes, counters or other small object onto a table. Count how many there are.

Fill in the table to show a half, a quarter and three-quarters of the amount. Repeat 5 times.

Amount	$\frac{1}{2}$	$\frac{1}{4}$	$\frac{3}{4}$

Measuring lengths in cm

A ruler is a tool for measuring objects. Most rulers can be used to measure in centimetres.
To use a ruler, place the 0cm end of the ruler at one end of your object. Make sure the object lines up with the ruler and use your hand to hold it in place.
Read the number that lines up with the other end of the object to get your measurement.

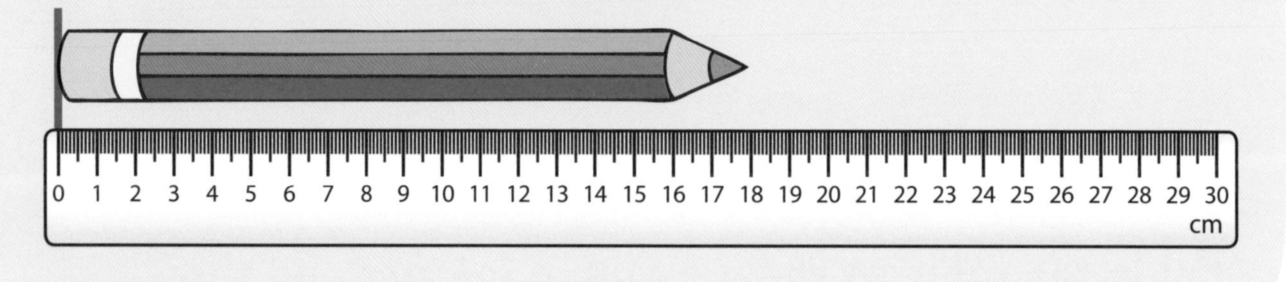

Use a ruler to measure the length of each object in cm.

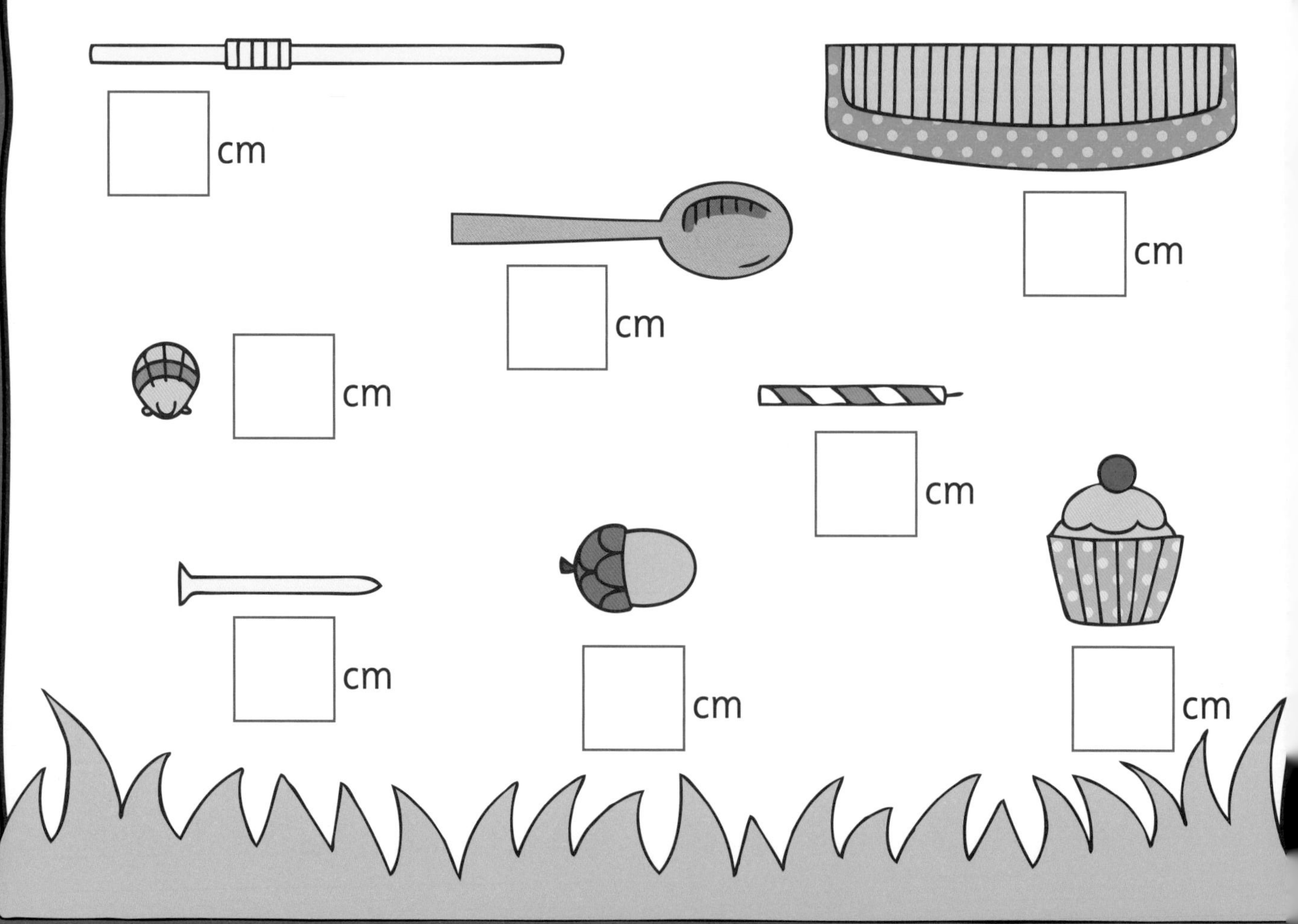

Weighing in kg and g

A litre bottle filled with water has about the same mass as 1 kilogram.
A paper clip has about the same mass as 1 gram.
Use this knowledge to help you estimate the mass of heavier or lighter objects.
Tip: There are 1000g in 1kg.

Choose five things to weigh.

1. Estimate first.

2. Write your estimate.

3. Use kitchen scales to weigh your item in kg and g.

4. Write your measurement.

I am going to weigh	Estimate	Mass

Measuring capacity using l and ml

A milk bottle has a capacity of 1 litre and a teaspoon has a capacity of about 5ml.
Use this knowledge to help you estimate the capacity of larger and smaller containers.
Tip: There are 1000ml in 1 litre.

Choose six different-sized containers to measure.

1. Write your estimate for each container.

2. Measure the container and write the capacity in l and ml. Use a measuring jug and a 5ml teaspoon.

Container	My estimate	My measure

Measuring temperature

We use a thermometer to measure temperature. Temperature is usually measured in degrees Celsius (°C).

The temperature is 15°C

1. Write the correct temperature for each thermometer.

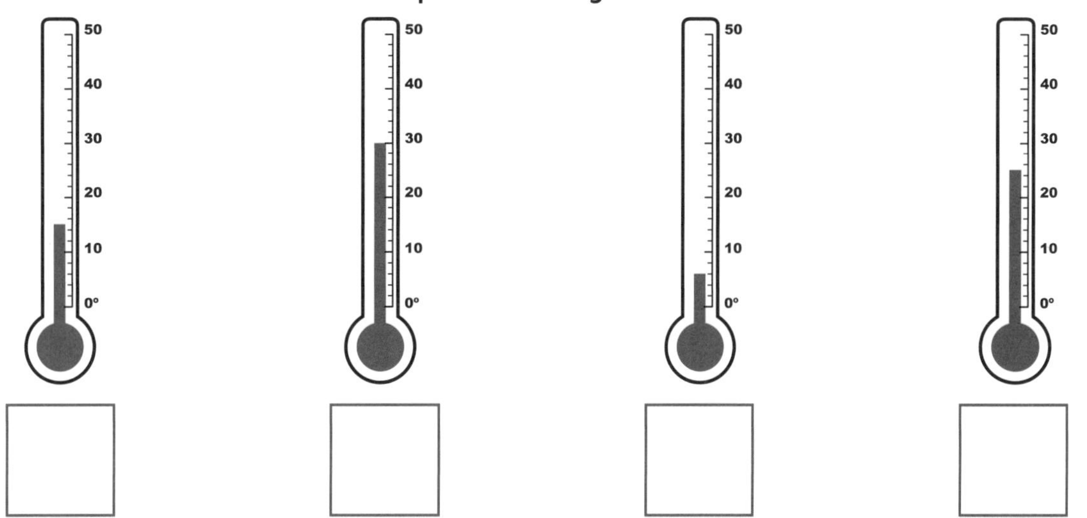

2. Mark each thermometer to show the correct temperature.

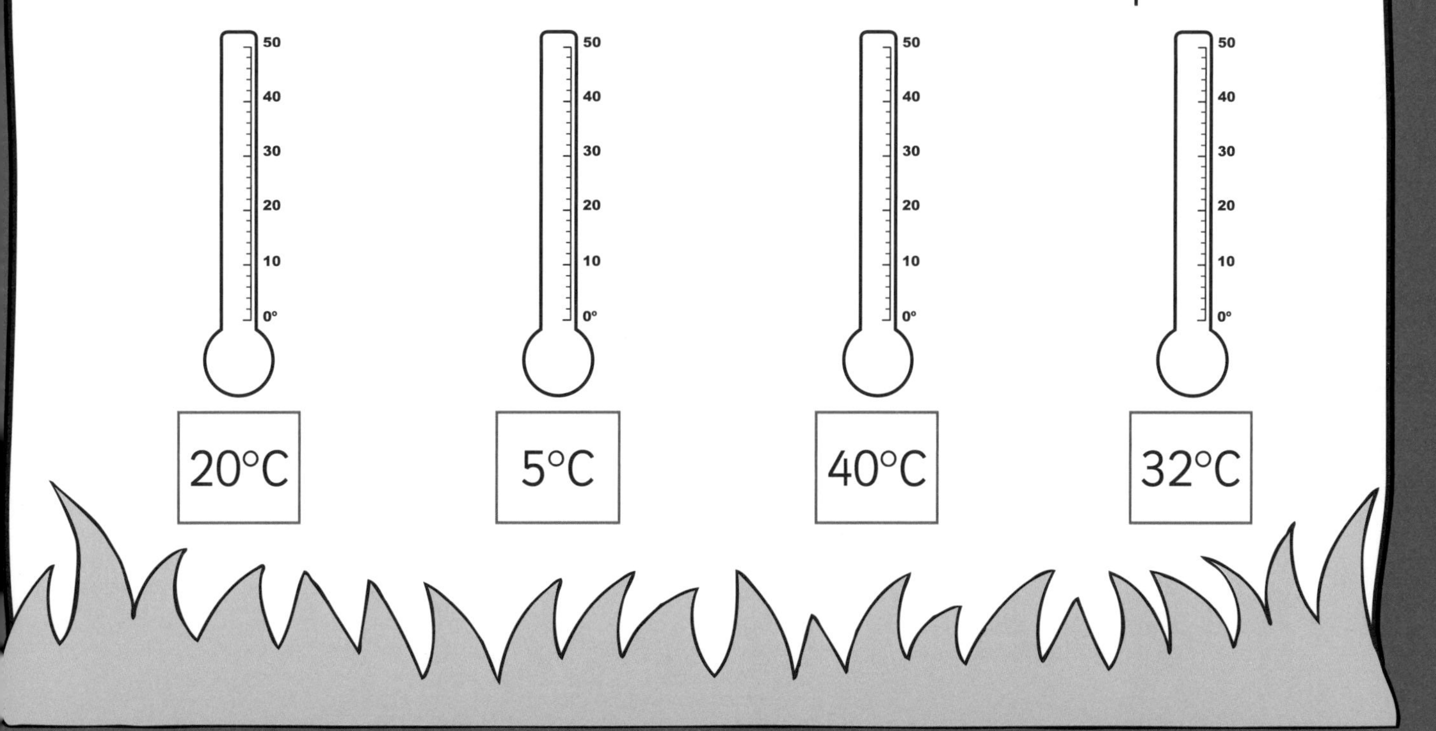

Comparing measures

When you order objects, ask yourself: Which is the heaviest/ lightest? Which is the next heaviest? You can use real objects to compare more accurately.

1. Order these objects from lightest to heaviest.

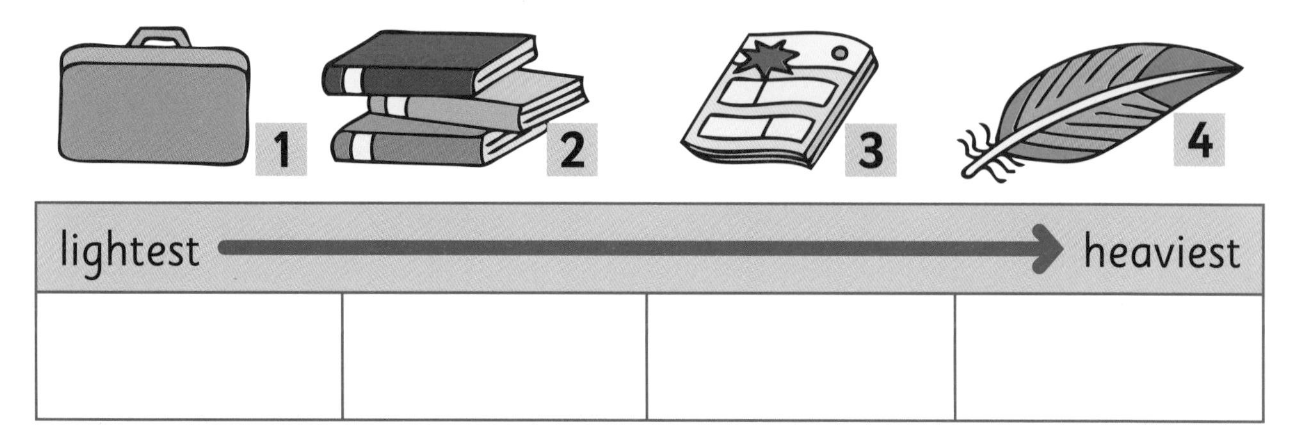

2. Find an object which = the mass of a banana.

____

3. Order these objects from shortest to longest.

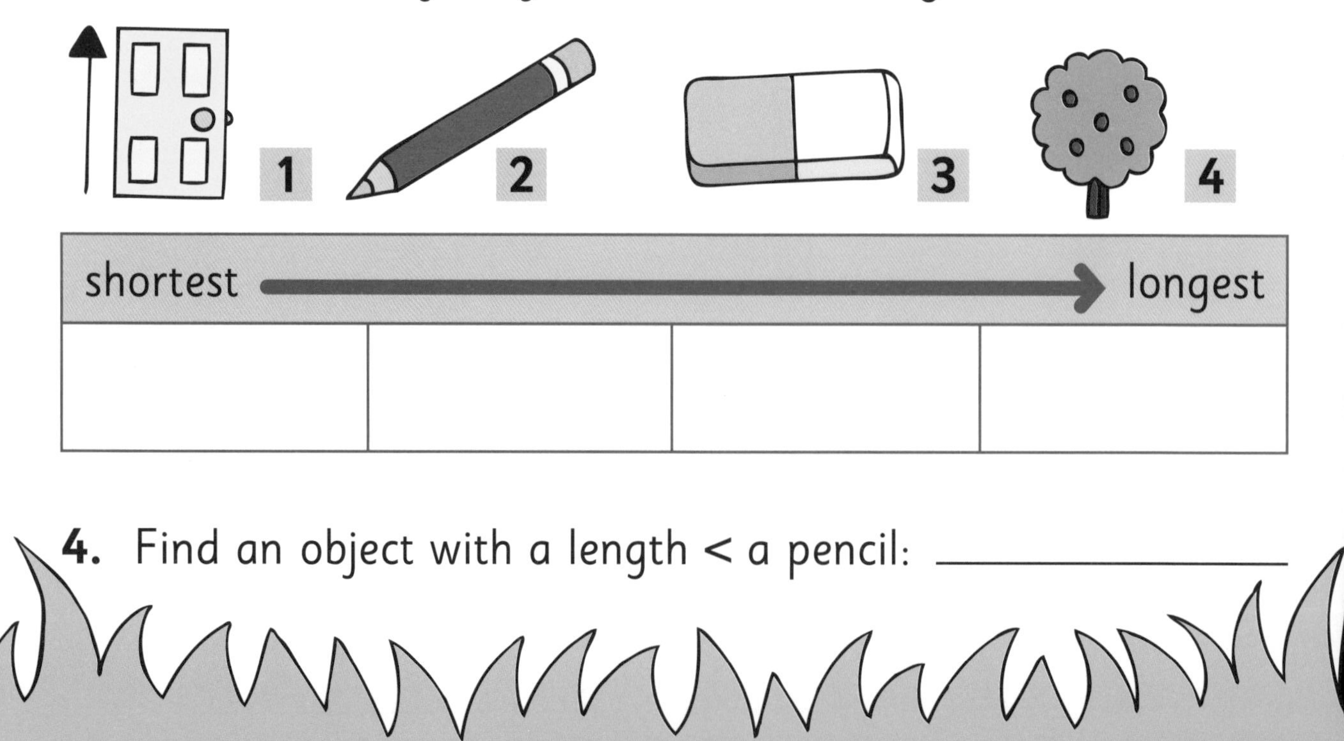

4. Find an object with a length $<$ a pencil: ____________________

5. Order these objects from smallest capacity to biggest capacity.

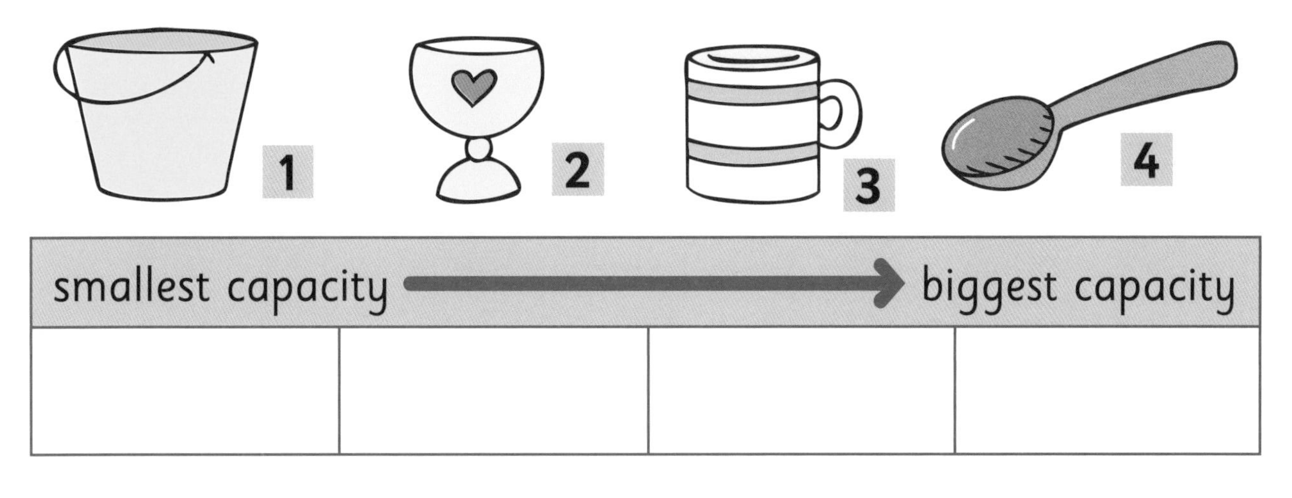

6. Find an object with a capacity which is $>$ a mug.

____

7. Order these objects from coldest to hottest.

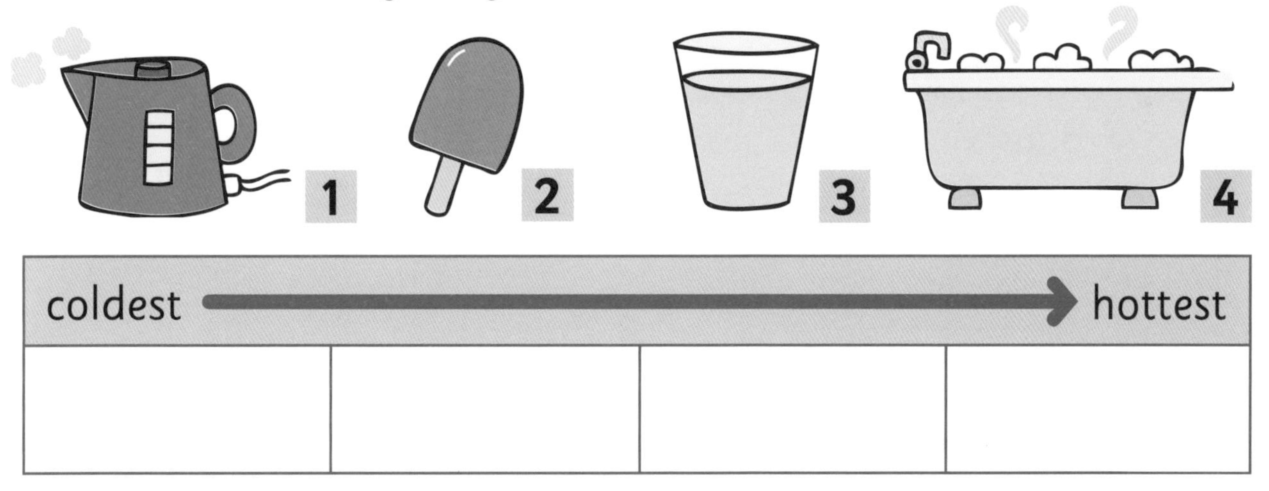

8. Find something with a temperature $<$ a kettle but $>$ than a glass of juice.

____

Time intervals

Think about different units of time.
Practice working out how many seconds there are in a minute, days in a week or weeks in a year.
Use a calendar to help you.

Draw a line to match each pair.

Telling the time

Practise telling the time to the hour, then to half-hour and quarter-hour intervals.

Learn to match  with 3:00

Remember: The big hand measures the minutes.
The little hand measures the hours.

Draw lines to connect the matching clock faces to the correct times.

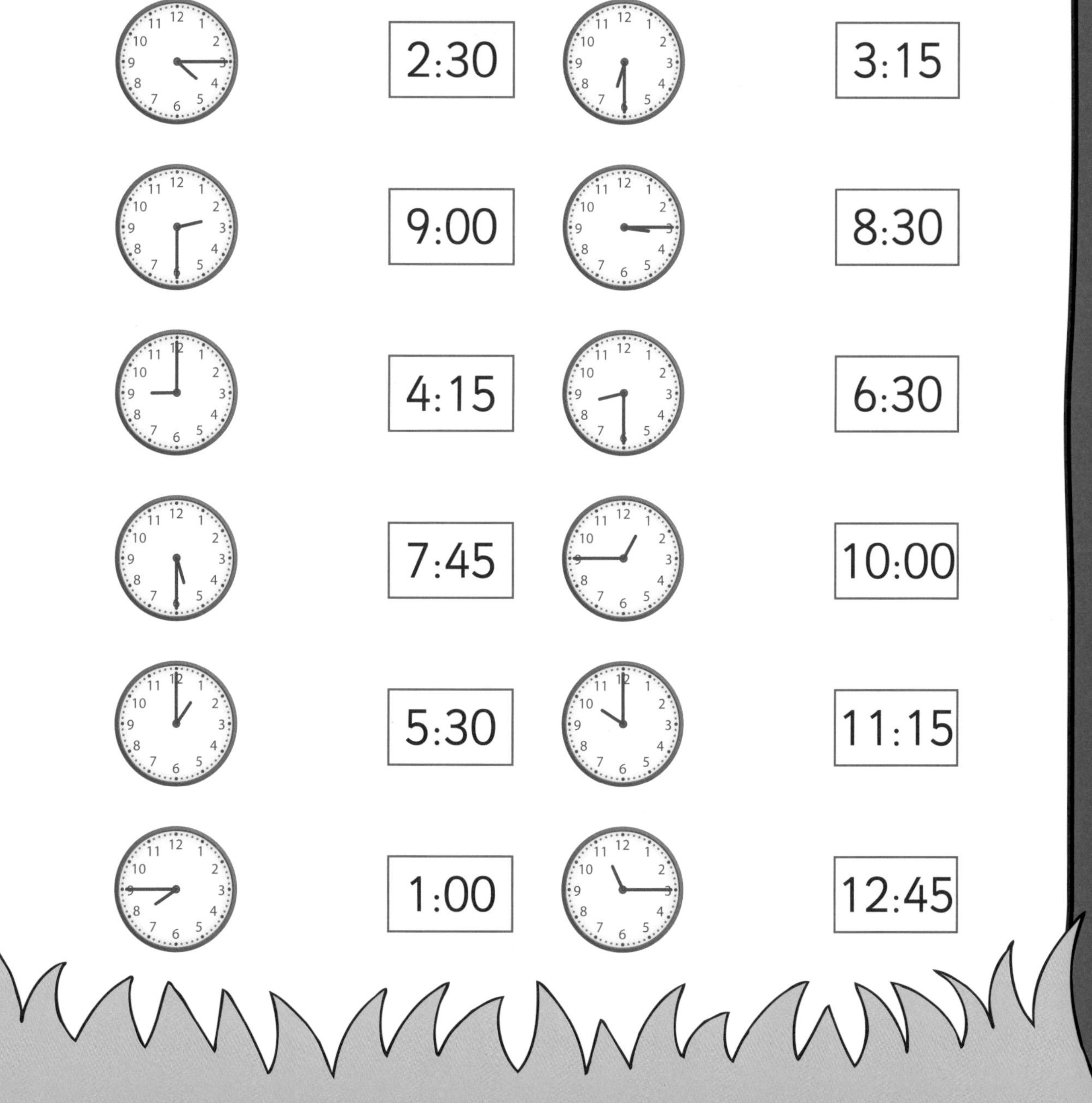

Pence to pounds

Tip: 100p = £1.00. The pounds and the pence are separated by a full stop.

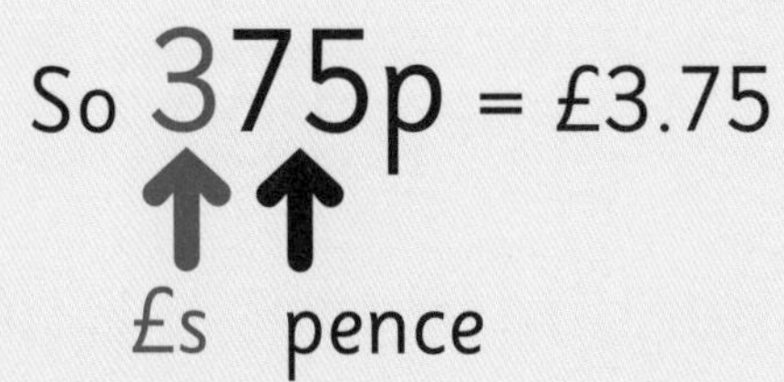

To add amounts of money, work out the answer mentally and then use real coins to check your answer.

Look at the numbers below. For each example, change the number of pence into pounds and pence.

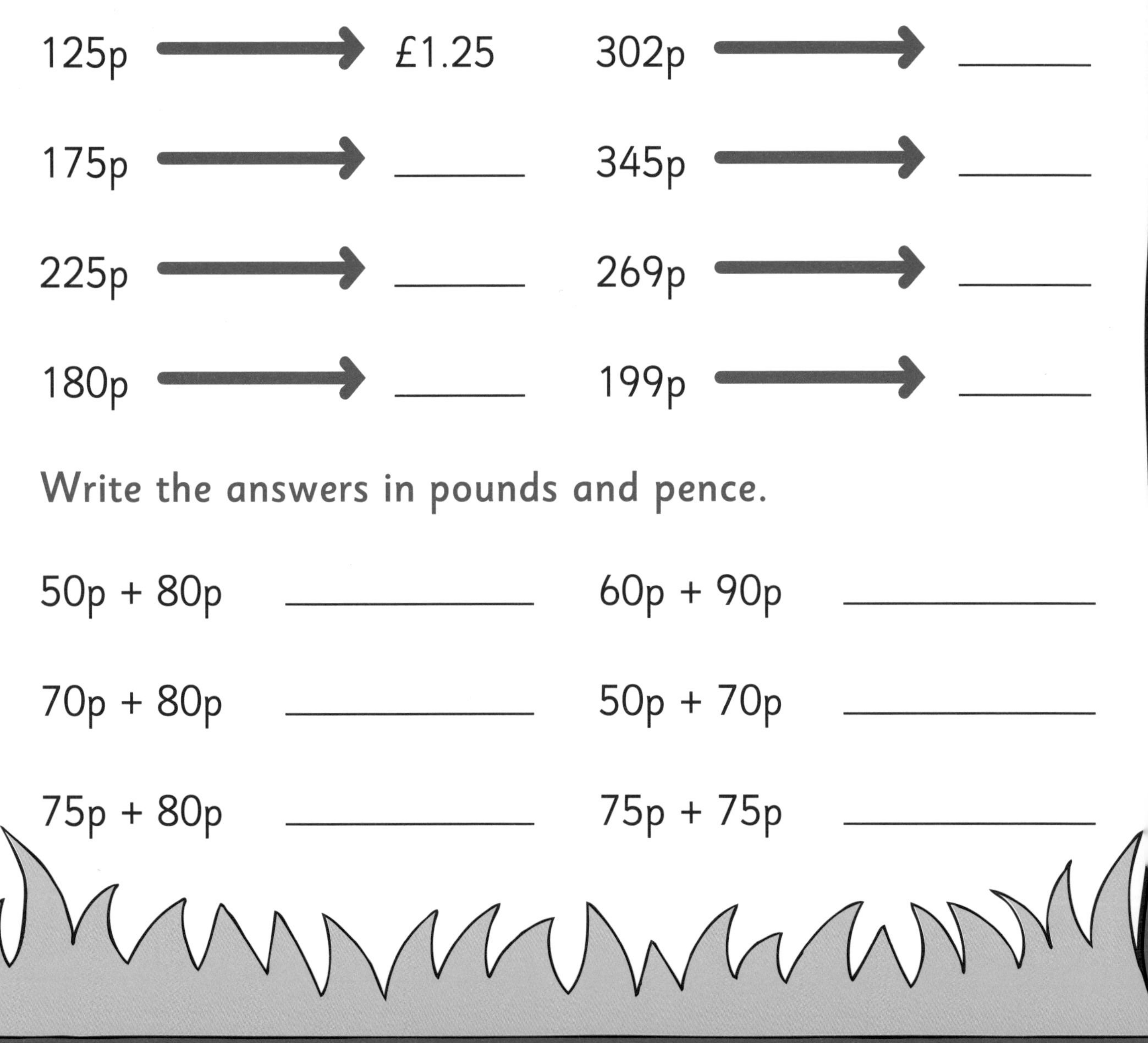

125p → £1.25

302p → ______

175p → ______

345p → ______

225p → ______

269p → ______

180p → ______

199p → ______

Write the answers in pounds and pence.

50p + 80p ______

60p + 90p ______

70p + 80p ______

50p + 70p ______

75p + 80p ______

75p + 75p ______

Different coins, same amount

Make different amounts using different coins.
To make 75p using the fewest coins, you need a 50p, 20p and 5p. There are many other ways of making 75p.

1. Eddie bought a comic for 20p. He paid for it exactly with silver coins. There are several different ways he can do it. Can you find them all?

____

____

____

____

2. A drink costs 74p. What is the fewest number of coins I could use to pay?

____

Find two other ways of paying.

____

Describe me

Count the number of sides and corners of each shape.

- Does it have straight or curved sides?
- Is it symmetrical – can you fold it in half exactly?
- Is it a pentagon, a hexagon or an octagon? What is the same about the two octagons? What is different?

1. Sides: ____ Symmetrical: ______

Corners: ____ Name: __________________

2. Sides: ____ Symmetrical: ______

Corners: ____ Name: __________________

3. Sides: ____ Symmetrical: ______

Corners: ____ Name: __________________

4. Sides: ____ Symmetrical: ______

Corners: ____ Name: __________________

5. Sides: ____ Symmetrical: ______

Corners: ____ Name: __________________

Faces of 3D shapes

3D or solid shapes have faces which are 2D shapes.
They could be squares, rectangles, circles, triangles,
pentagons, hexagons and other shapes.

Look at the 3D shapes. What 2D shape is the face coloured in dark blue? Write its name on the line.

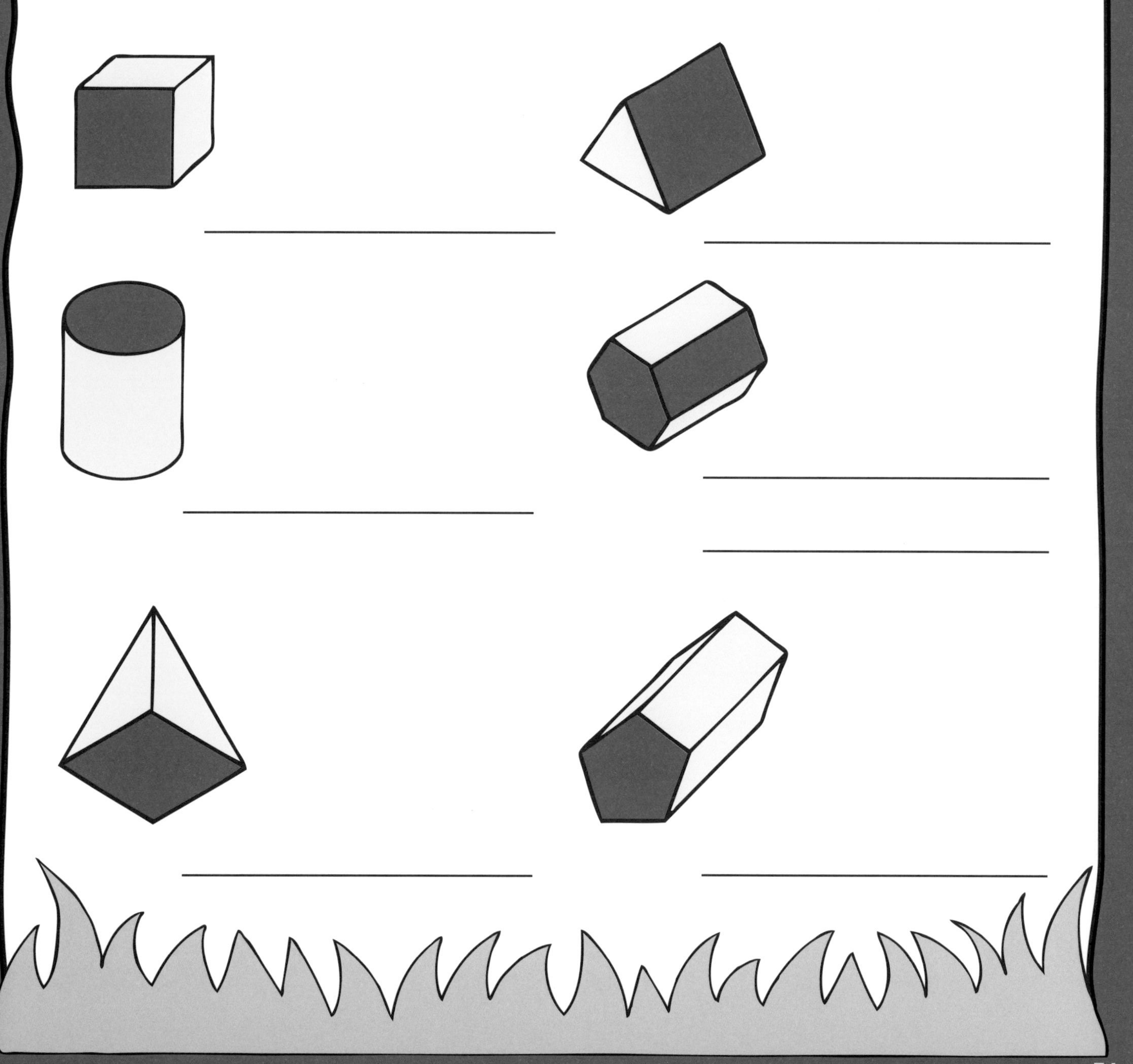

Sorting 2D shapes

Draw a line from each shape to the correct shape name.

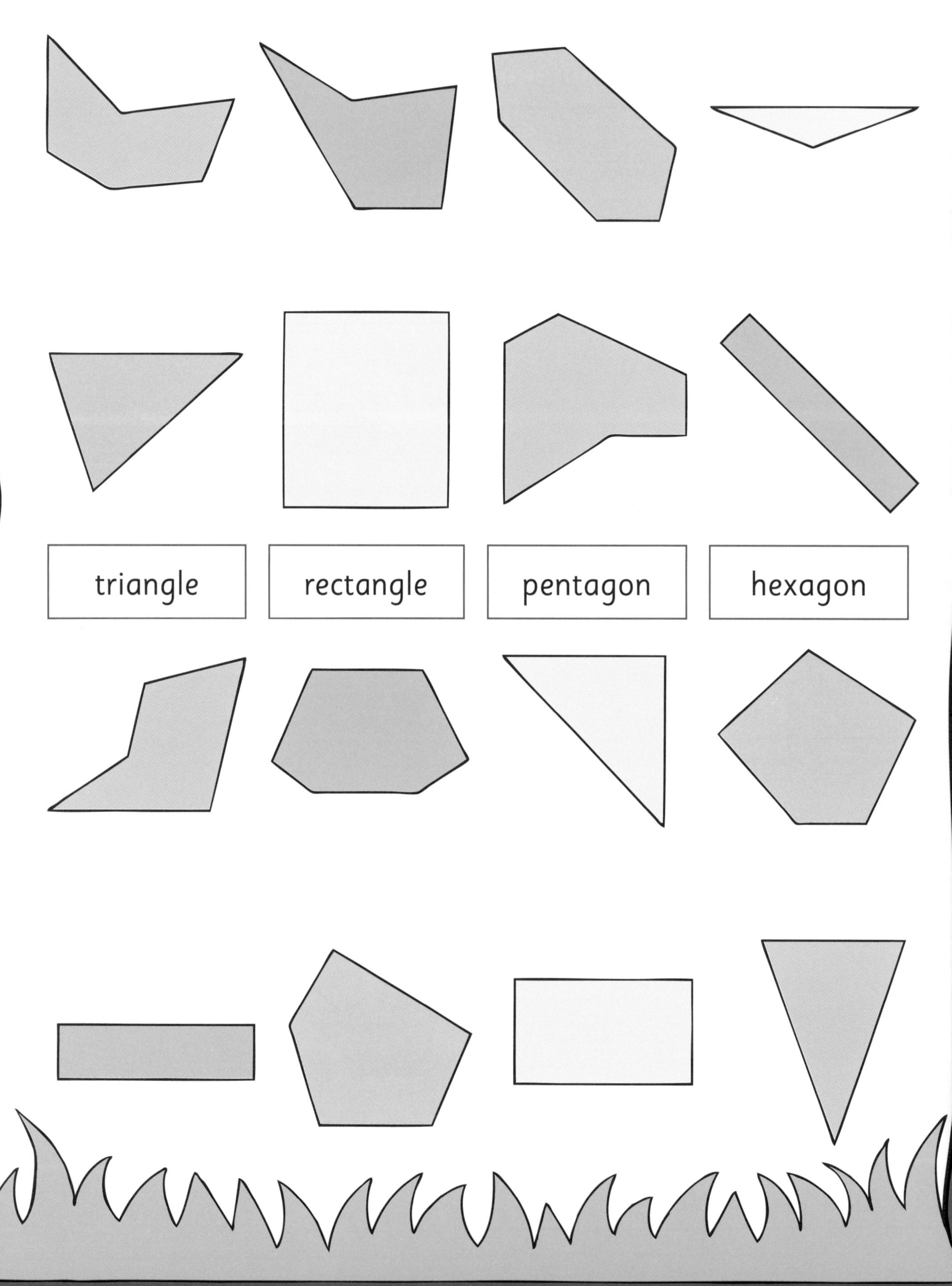

Sorting 3D shapes

Count the faces to help you sort these 3D shapes. Tick each shape as you sort it, so you don't miss any out.

1. Name each shape. Here are the words you will need.

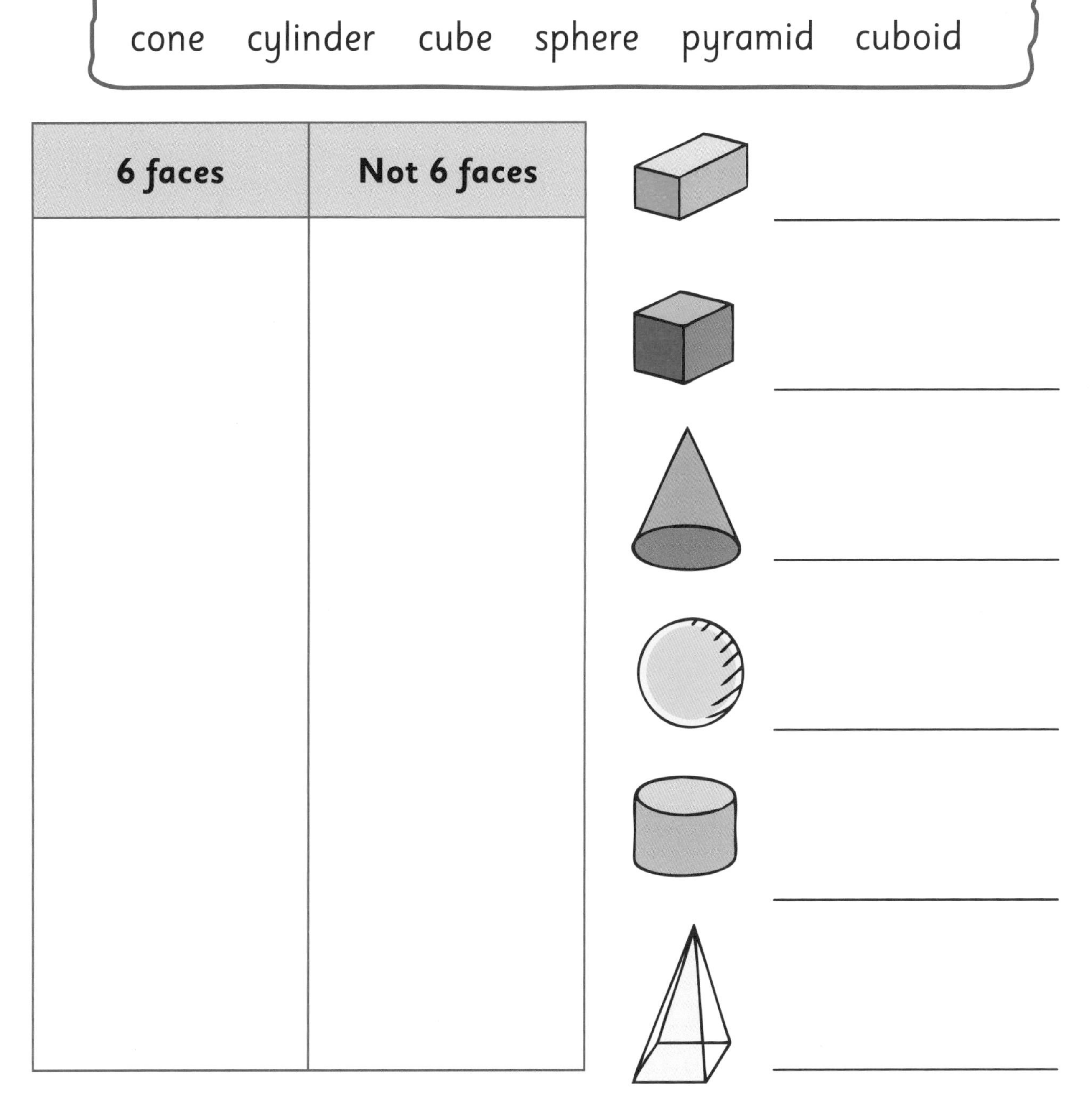

6 faces	Not 6 faces

2. Write the names to show where each 3D shape should go in the Carroll diagram.

Where am I heading?

If you turn **clockwise**, you turn in the same direction as clock hands. If you turn **anti-clockwise**, you turn in the opposite direction.

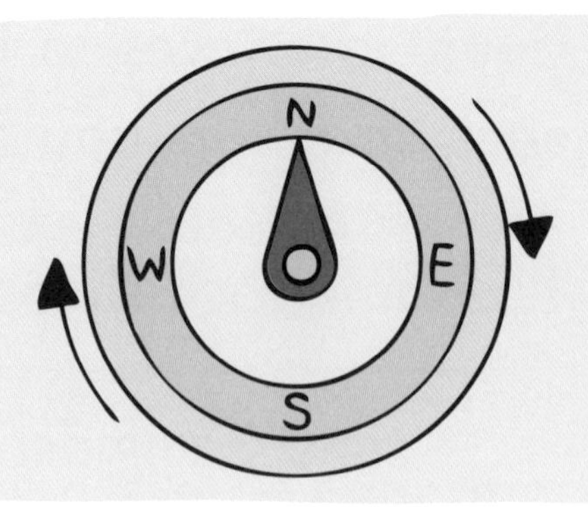

1. I am facing north. I take a quarter turn anti-clockwise. Which direction am I facing now?

____

2. I am facing south. I take a half turn clockwise. Which direction am I facing now?

____

3. I am facing east. I take a three-quarter turn anti-clockwise. Which direction am I facing now?

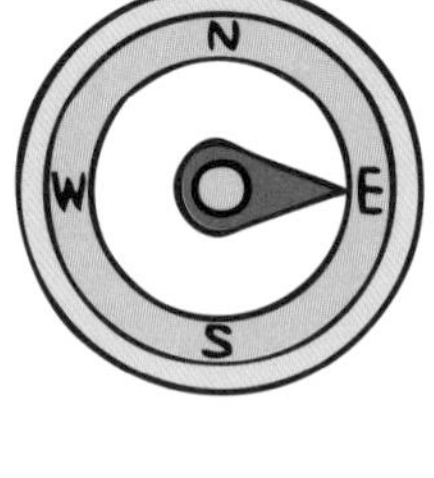

____

4. I am facing west. I take a three-quarter turn clockwise. Which direction am I facing now?

____

Directions

Program Robo-dog to rescue his owner. He must lead his owner to the forest entrance.

Starting at the forest entrance, give Robo-dog his commands to get back to his owner and then bring him back. Write down each command.

- Robo-dog can only move in straight lines.
- He cannot move through the trees.
- Explain carefully in what direction he should travel, such as 'Move forward two squares. Make a quarter turn clockwise.'

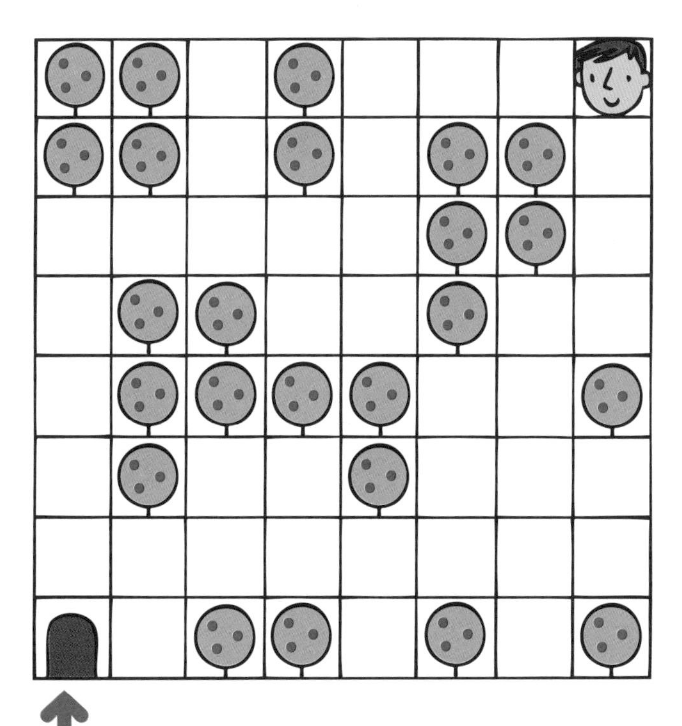

Forest entrance

Tally charts

A tally chart is a table which shows how many times something happens.

卌 = 5

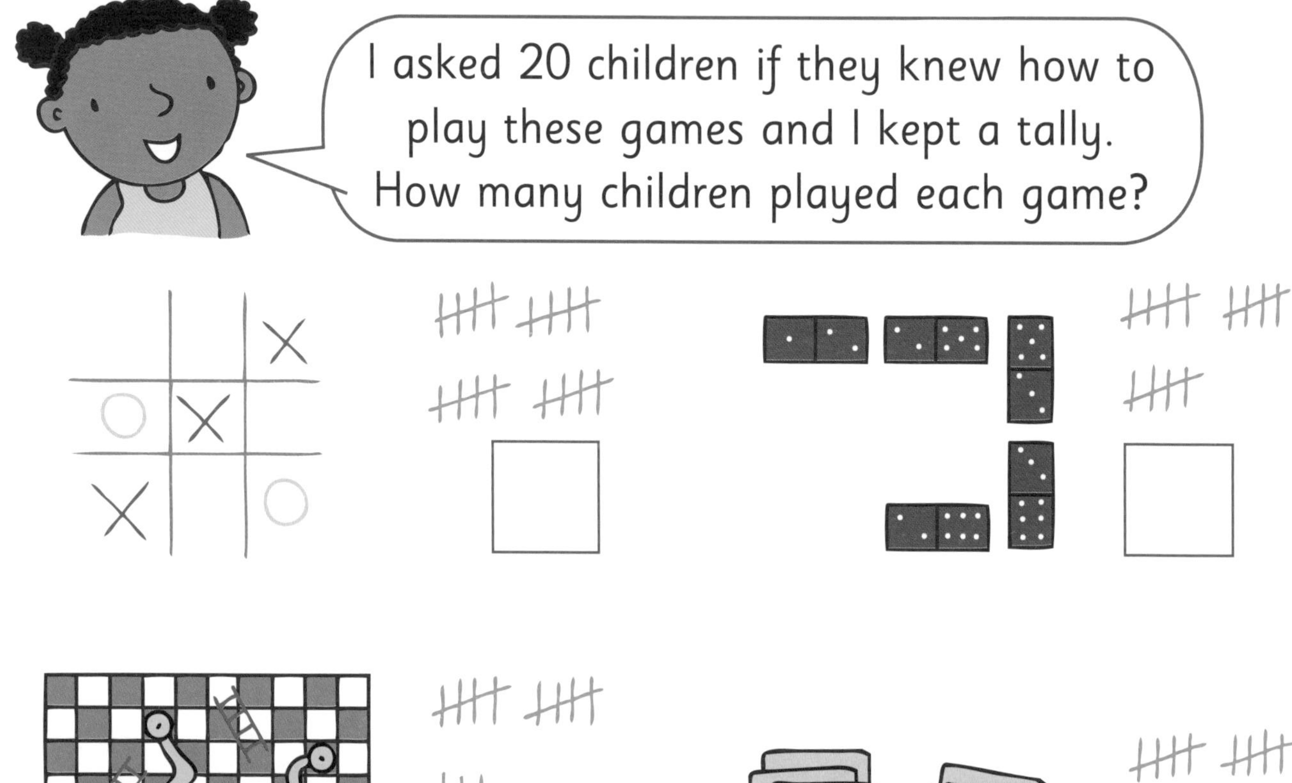

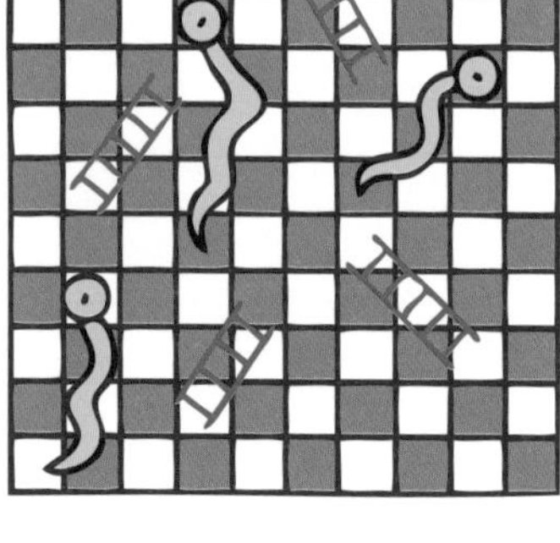

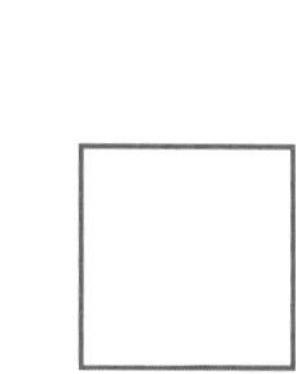

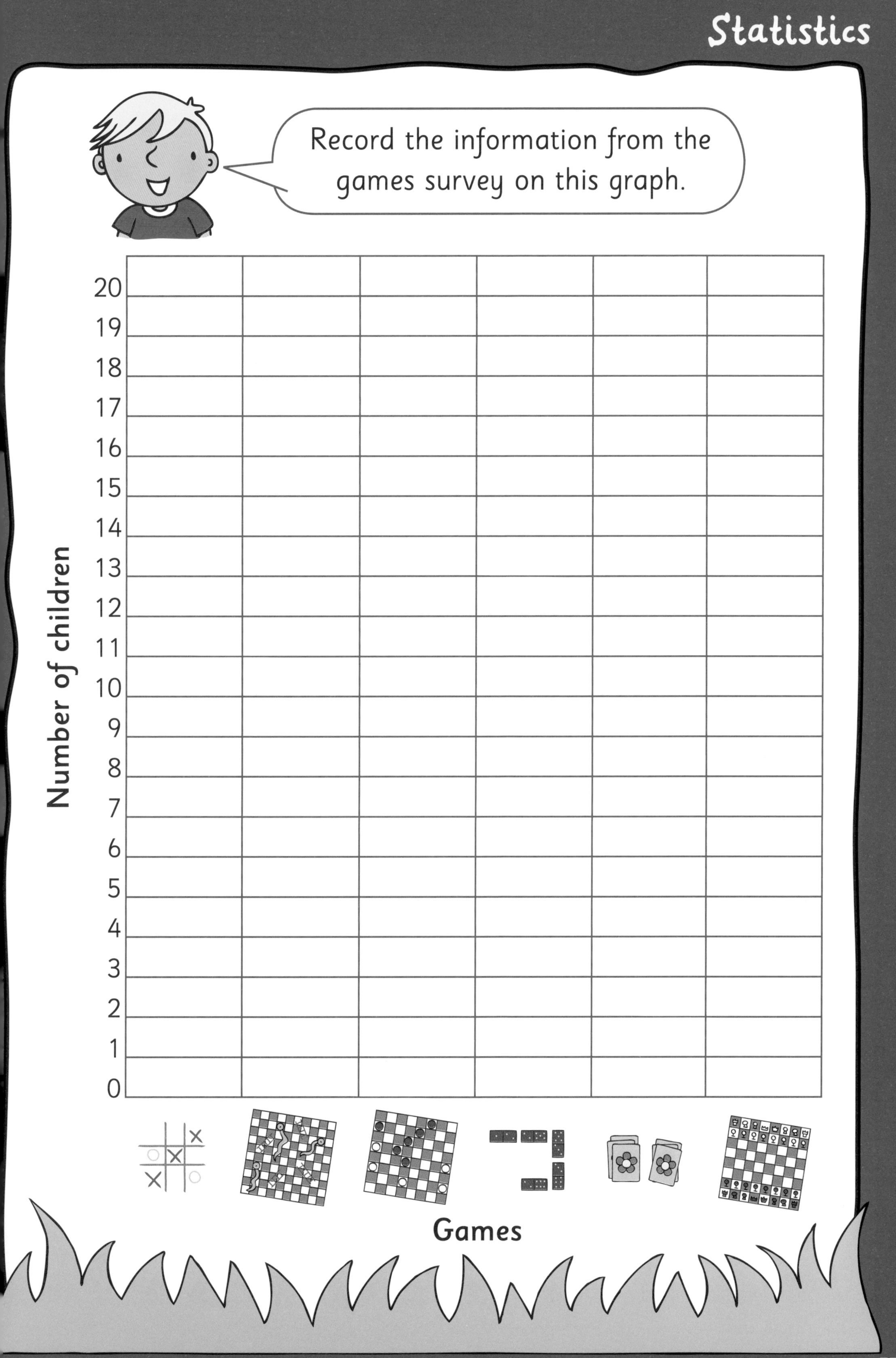
Record the information from the games survey on this graph.
Number of children
20
19
18
17
16
15
14
13
12
11
10
9
8
7
6
5
4
3
2
1
0
Games

Drawing a block graph

In a **block graph** one block represents one item of data.

Problem

I would like to order some paint for art, but I need you to help me decide which three colours to buy. I asked the class to tell me their favourite colours, and this is what they said:

2 liked black   3 liked orange   4 liked red

1 liked green   10 liked yellow   6 liked white

Draw the results as a block graph.

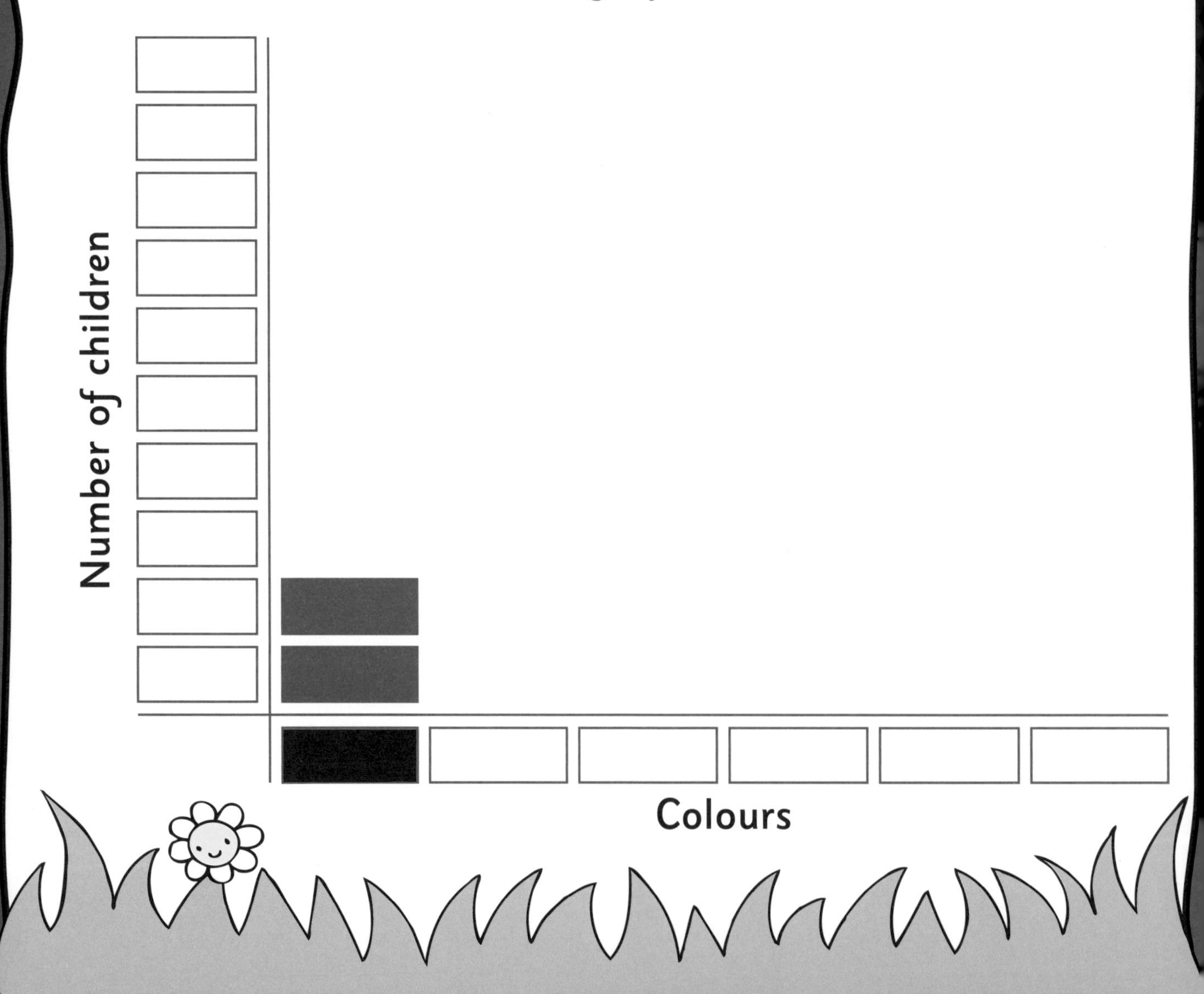

Take-away pictogram

A **pictogram** uses symbols to represent data. It must have a **key** to show how many items each symbol represents.

Josh did a survey to find out which was the most popular take-away food. Here are his results:

- 5 children liked pizza (p)
- 3 children liked burgers (b)
- 9 children like fish and chips (f and c)
- 4 children liked Chinese (Ch)
- 6 children liked curry (c)
- 2 children liked hotdogs (h)

Use this information to complete the pictogram below.

Key: ☺ = 1 child

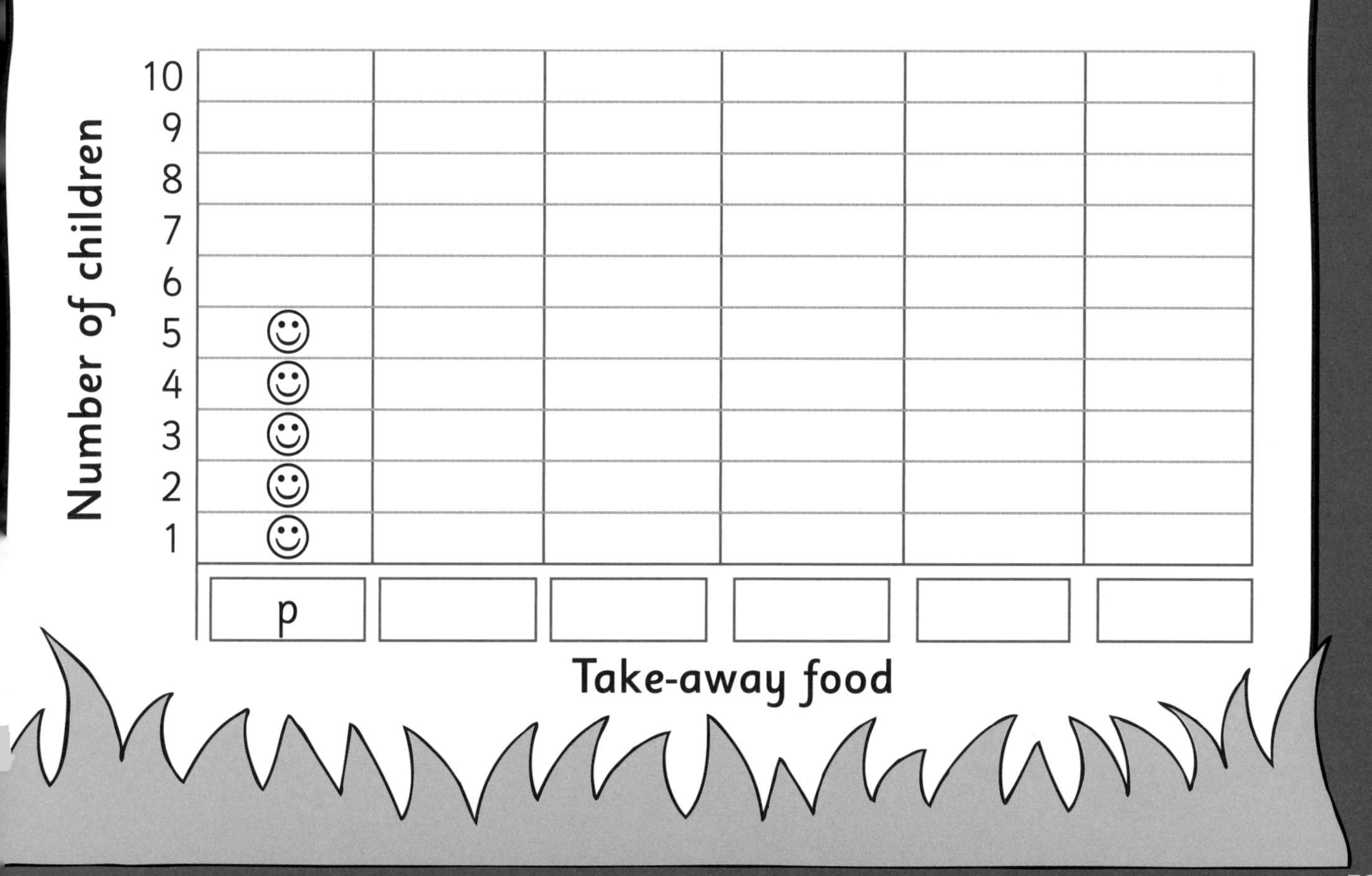

Progress chart

Making progress? Tick (✔) the flower boxes as you complete each section of the book.

Answers

The answers are given below. They are referenced by page number and where applicable, question number. The answers usually only include the information the children are expected to give.

<table>
<tr><th>Page number</th><th>Question number</th><th>Answers</th></tr>
<tr><td>6</td><td></td><td>28, 29, 30
50, 60, 70
48, 50, 52
56, 57, 58
100, 110, 120
70, 72, 74</td></tr>
<tr><td>7</td><td></td><td>40, 38, 36, 34, 32, 30, 28, 26, 24, 22
10, 15, 20, 25, 30, 35, 40, 45, 50, 55
60, 55, 50, 45, 40, 35, 30, 25, 20, 15
20, 30, 40, 50, 60, 70, 80, 90, 100, 110
90, 80, 70, 60, 50, 40, 30, 20, 10, 0</td></tr>
<tr><td>8</td><td></td><td>40 + 2 = 42   30 + 2 = 32
40 + 5 = 45   30 + 5 = 35
40 + 7 = 47   30 + 7 = 37
10 + 1 = 11   70 + 1 = 71
10 + 2 = 12   70 + 2 = 72
10 + 5 = 15   70 + 5 = 75
10 + 7 = 17   70 + 7 = 77
30 + 1 = 31</td></tr>
<tr><td>9</td><td></td><td><table>
<tr><th></th><th>100s</th><th>10s</th><th>1s</th></tr>
<tr><td>seventy-eight</td><td>0</td><td>7</td><td>8</td></tr>
<tr><td>forty-seven</td><td>0</td><td>4</td><td>7</td></tr>
<tr><td>one hundred and twenty-three</td><td>1</td><td>2</td><td>3</td></tr>
<tr><td>one hundred and four</td><td>1</td><td>0</td><td>4</td></tr>
<tr><td></td><td>3</td><td>6</td><td>0</td></tr>
</table></td></tr>
<tr><td>10</td><td></td><td>23, 38, 45, 57, 69, 70, 89, 94
Check children's drawings</td></tr>
<tr><td>11</td><td>1</td><td>7, 18, 25, 33, 41, 59, 67, 73, 80, 92</td></tr>
<tr><td></td><td>2</td><td>14kg, 22kg, 31kg, 43kg, 45kg, 50kg</td></tr>
<tr><td></td><td>3</td><td>49cm, 41cm, 33cm, 20cm, 17cm, 16cm,</td></tr>
<tr><td>12–13</td><td>1</td><td><</td></tr>
<tr><td></td><td>2</td><td>></td></tr>
<tr><td></td><td>3</td><td>></td></tr>
<tr><td></td><td>4</td><td><</td></tr>
<tr><td></td><td>5</td><td>=</td></tr>
<tr><td></td><td>6</td><td>></td></tr>
<tr><td></td><td>7</td><td>=</td></tr>
<tr><td></td><td>8</td><td><</td></tr>
<tr><td></td><td>9</td><td><</td></tr>
<tr><td></td><td>10</td><td>></td></tr>
<tr><td></td><td>1</td><td>False</td></tr>
<tr><td></td><td>2</td><td>True</td></tr>
<tr><td></td><td>3</td><td>False</td></tr>
<tr><td></td><td>4</td><td>False</td></tr>
<tr><td></td><td>1</td><td>></td></tr>
<tr><td></td><td>2</td><td><</td></tr>
<tr><td></td><td>3</td><td>></td></tr>
</table>

Page number	Question number	Answers	
14		The bear is on number 3	The camel is on number 7
		The dog is on number 6	The cat is on number 8
		The bear is on number 20	The camel is on number 15
		The dog is on number 5	The cat is on number 42
15		30 strawberries	
		35 butterflies	
		12 shells	
		27 fish	
16		73, seventy-three	42, forty-two
		23, twenty-three	43, forty-three
		24, twenty-four	47, forty-seven
		27, twenty-seven	48, forty-eight
		28, twenty-eight	74, seventy-four
		32, thirty-two	78, seventy-eight
		34, thirty-four	82, eighty-two
		37, thirty-seven	83, eighty-three
		38, thirty-eight	84, eighty-four
		72, seventy-two	87, eighty-seven
17	1a	7 boxes, 2 pencils left over	
	1b	3 boxes, 8 pencils left over	
	1c	5 boxes, 6 pencils left over	
	1d	10 boxes, 3 pencils left over	
	2a	27	
	2b	43	
	2c	91	
18		1 + 19	6 + 14
		2 + 18	7 + 13
		3 + 17	8 + 12
		4 + 16	9 + 11
		5 + 15	10 + 10
19		19, 1	14, 6
		18, 2	13, 7
		17, 3	12, 8
		16, 4	11, 9
		15, 5	10, 10
20		10 + 90	40 + 60
		20 + 80	50 + 50
		30 + 70	

Page number	Question number	Answers
21	1	Accept any suitable answer
		1 + 99 26 + 74
		2 + 98 27 + 73
		3 + 97 28 + 72
		4 + 96 29 + 71
		5 + 95 30 + 70
		6 + 94 31 + 69
		7 + 93 32 + 68
		8 + 92 33 + 67
		9 + 91 34 + 66
		10 + 90 35 + 65
		11 + 89 36 + 64
		12 + 88 37 + 63
		13 + 87 38 + 62
		14 + 86 39 + 61
		15 + 85 40 + 60
		16 + 84 41 + 59
		17 + 83 42 + 58
		18 + 82 43 + 57
		19 + 81 44 + 56
		20 + 80 45 + 55
		21 + 79 46 + 54
		22 + 78 47 + 53
		23 + 77 48 + 52
		24 + 76 49 + 51
		25 + 75 50 + 50
22	1a	19, 5, 14, 14
	1b	18, 7, 11, 11
	2a	29, 12, 12, 12
	2b	80, 50, 30, 30
23		3 + 2 = 5 and 5 – 2 = 3 5 + 10 = 15 and 15 – 10 = 5 14 + 5 = 19 and 19 – 5 = 14 11 + 10 = 21 and 21 – 10 = 11 13 + 12 = 25 and 25 – 12 = 13 15 + 20 = 35 and 35 – 20 = 15 16 + 30 = 46 and 46 – 30 = 16 20 + 23 = 43 and 43 – 23 = 20 24 + 35 = 59 and 59 – 35 = 24 26 + 32 = 58 and 58 – 32 = 26
24	1b	11 + 8 = 19
	1c	16 + 3 = 19
	1d	14 + 6 = 20
	1e	12 + 5 = 17
	1f	17 + 3 = 20
	2	Answers will vary, for example: 21 + 11 = 32 44 + 11 = 55 42 + 13 = 55
25		Answers will vary, for example:

Numbers chosen	Numbers totalling 10	Addition
2, 8, 3	2 + 8 = 10	2 + 8 + 3 = 13
2, 8, 4	2 + 8 = 10	2 + 8 + 4 = 14

Page number	Question number	Answers
26	1	6 + 4 + 3 6 + 5 + 2 6 + 4 + 2 + 1
	2	6, 5, 1 5, 4, 3 6, 4, 2 6, 3, 3 4, 4, 4 5, 5, 2

Page number	Question number	Answers
27	1	17 boys
	2	8 yellow balloons
	3	15 were in boxes
	4	6 were spotty
	5	9 were cheese
	6	13 were orange
28–29		2 + 2 + 2 + 2, 2 × 4 = 8 2 + 2 + 2 + 2 + 2 + 2, 2 × 6 = 12 2 + 2 + 2 + 2 + 2 + 2 + 2, 2 × 7 = 14 2 + 2 + 2 + 2 + 2 + 2 + 2 + 2, 2 × 8 = 16 8 – 2 – 2 – 2 – 2, 8 ÷ 2 = 4 10 – 2 – 2 – 2 – 2 – 2, 10 ÷ 2 = 5 12 – 2 – 2 – 2 – 2 – 2 – 2, 12 ÷ 2 = 6
30–31		5 + 5 + 5 + 5, 5 × 4 = 20 5 + 5 + 5 + 5 + 5 + 5, 5 × 6 = 30 5 + 5 + 5 + 5 + 5 + 5 + 5, 5 × 7 = 35 5 + 5 + 5 + 5 + 5 + 5 + 5 + 5 + 5, 5 × 9 = 45 15 – 5 – 5 – 5, 15 ÷ 5 = 3 25 – 5 – 5 – 5 – 5 – 5, 25 ÷ 5 = 5 35 – 5 – 5 – 5 – 5 – 5 – 5 – 5, 35 ÷ 5 = 7 50 – 5 – 5 – 5 – 5 – 5 – 5 – 5 – 5 – 5 – 5, 50 ÷ 5 = 10
32	1	

×	2	5	10
2	4	10	20
4	8	20	40
1	2	5	10
5	10	25	50

Page number	Question number	Answers
32	2	

×	2	5	10
7	14	35	70
6	12	30	60
3	6	15	30
8	16	40	80

Page number	Question number	Answers
33		5 × 2 = 10 2 × 7 = 14 10 × 3 = 30 5 × 4 = 20 6 × 10 = 60 10 × 5 = 50 5 × 8 = 40
34	1b	1 × 2 = 2
	1c	2 × 4 = 8
	1d	5 × 2 = 10
	1e	3 × 5 = 15
	1f	7 × 5 = 35
	1g	7 × 2 = 14
	1h	5 × 9 = 45
	1i	9 × 2 = 18
	2	Answers will vary, for example: 2 × 5p coins 10 × 1p 1 × 10p 5p + 1p + 1p + 1p + 1p + 1p 5p + 2p + 2p + 1p
35	1	6, 38, 42, 60, 102, 24
	2	25, 27, 29
	3	

	Multiples of 2	Multiples of 5
Odd numbers		15,25
Even numbers	8,30,42	30

Page number	Question number	Answers
36	1	2, 4 3, 2
	2	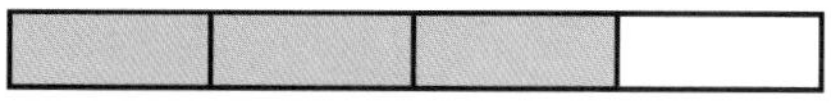
	3	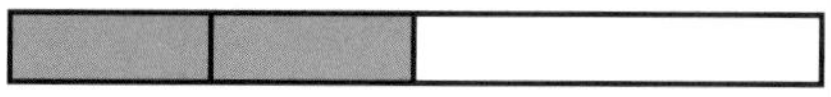
	4	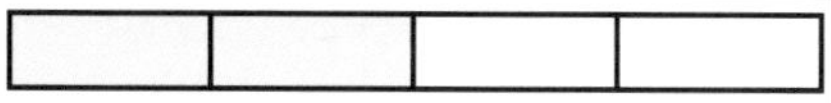
	5	$\frac{2}{4}$
37	1	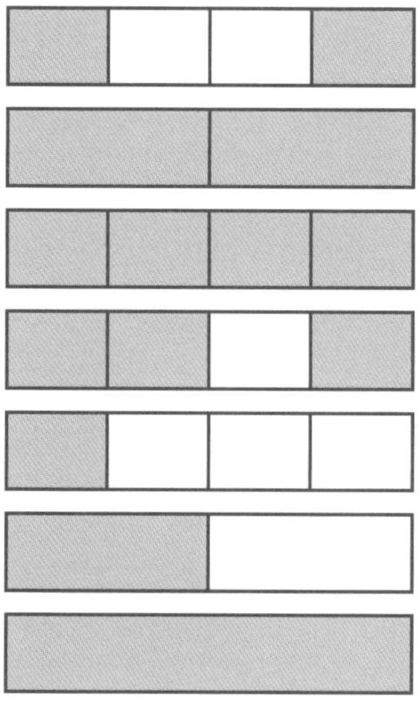 $\frac{2}{4}$ $\frac{2}{2}$ $\frac{4}{4}$ $\frac{3}{4}$ $\frac{1}{4}$ $\frac{1}{2}$ 1
	2	1 whole = $\frac{1}{2} + \frac{1}{2}$ $\frac{1}{2} = \frac{1}{4} + \frac{1}{4}$ $\frac{3}{4} = \frac{1}{2} + \frac{1}{4}$
38	1	Accept any variation of $\frac{3}{4}$ 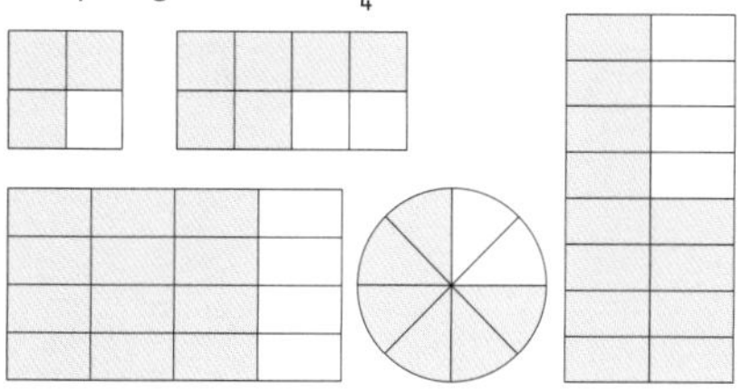
	2	3 books 6 apples 9 teddies 15 cars
39		Answers will vary.
40		Straw = 7cm Candle = 3cm Comb = 6cm Nail = 3cm Spoon = 5cm Acorn = 2cm Shell = 1cm Cake = 2cm
41		Answers will vary, check children's measurements.
42		Answers will vary, check children's measurements.
43	1	14°C, 30°C, 6°C, 24°C
	2	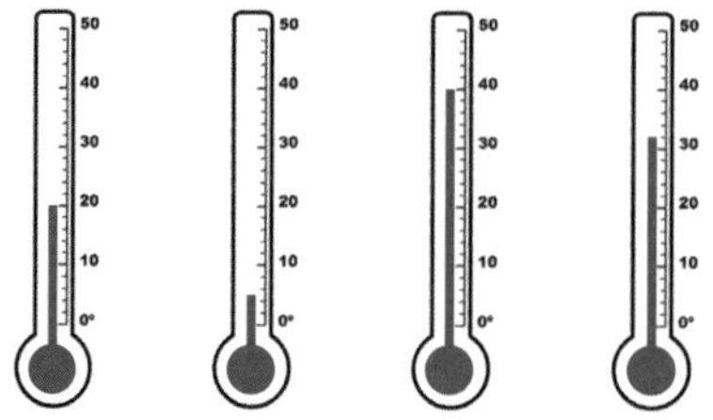

Page number	Question number	Answers
44–45	1	lightest → heaviest 4 feather, 3 comic, 2 pile of books, 1 suitcase
	2	Answers will vary.
	3	shortest → longest 3 rubber, 2 pencil, 1 door, 4 tree
	4	Answers will vary.
	5	biggest capacity 4 teaspoon, 2 egg cup, 3 mug, 1 bucket
	6	Answers will vary.
	7	coldest → hottest 2 ice lolly, 3 glass of water, 4 hot bath, 1 boliling kettle
	8	Answers will vary.
46		1 fortnight = 2 weeks 60 minutes = 1 hour 60 seconds = 1 minute 1 day = 24 hours 120 seconds = 2 minutes 7 days = 1 week 1 year = 52 weeks
47		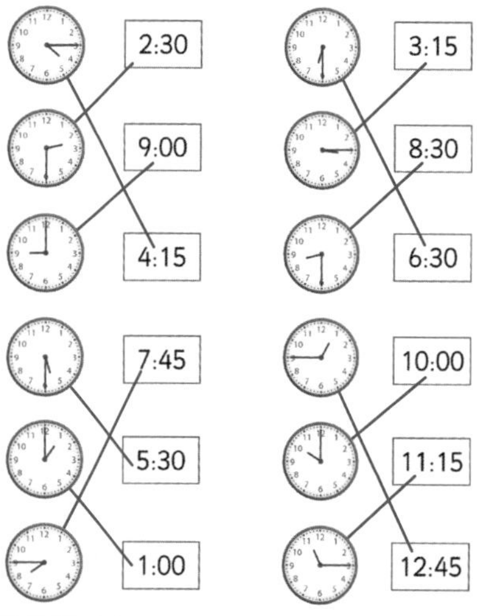 2:30, 9:00, 4:15 3:15, 8:30, 6:30 7:45, 5:30, 1:00 10:00, 11:15, 12:45
48		125p = £1.25 175p = £1.75 225p = £2.25 180p = £1.80 302p = £3.02 345p = £3.45 269p = £2.69 199p = £1.99 £1.30 £1.50 £1.50 £1.20 £1.55 £1.50
49	1	20p 10p + 10p 10p + 5p + 5p 5p + 5p + 5p + 5p
	2	4 = 50p, 20p, 2p, 2p Answers will vary, for example: = 20p + 20p + 20p + 10p + 2p + 2p = 50p + 10p + 10p + 2p + 2p
50	1	Sides: 6 Symmetrical: Yes Corners: 6 Name: Hexagon
	2	Sides: 8 Symmetrical: No Corners: 8 Name: Octagon
	3	Sides: 5 Symmetrical: No Corners: 5 Name: Pentagon
	4	Sides: 8 Symmetrical: Yes Corners: 8 Name: Octagon
	5	Sides: 5 Symmetrical: Yes Corners: 5 Name: Pentagon

Page number	Question number	Answers
51		square, rectangle circle, hexagon and rectangle square, pentagon
52		triangles 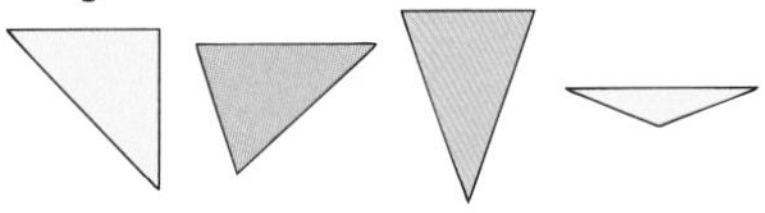 rectangles 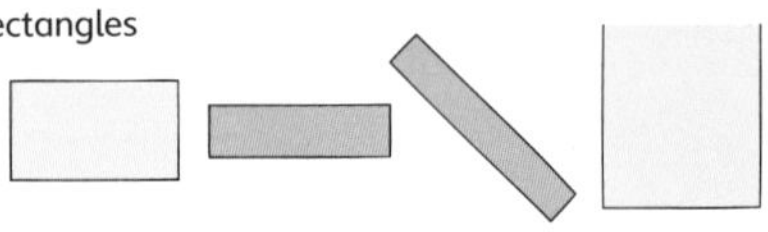 pentagons 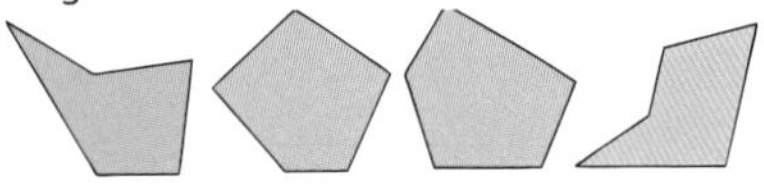 hexagons 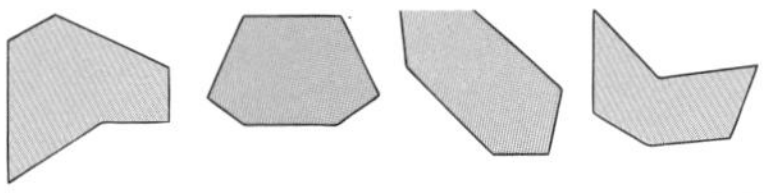
53	1	cuboid cube cone sphere cylinder pyramid
	2	**6 faces**: cube, cuboid **Not 6 faces**: cone, cylinder, sphere, pyramid
54	1	West
	2	North
	3	North
	4	South
55		Move forward 1 square. Make a quarter turn clockwise. Move forward 6 squares. Make a quarter turn anti-clockwise. Move forward 3 squares. Make a quarter turn clockwise. Move forward 1 square. Make a quarter turn anti-clockwise. Move forward 3 squares.
56–57		Noughts and Crosses = 20 Dominoes = 15 Snakes and Ladders = 13 Cards = 17 Draughts = 7 Chess = 3 Check children's drawings on the graph.
58		Number of children: 10, 9, 8, 7, 6, 5, 4, 3, 2, 1 Colours
59		Number of children p, b, f and c, Ch, c, h Take-away food

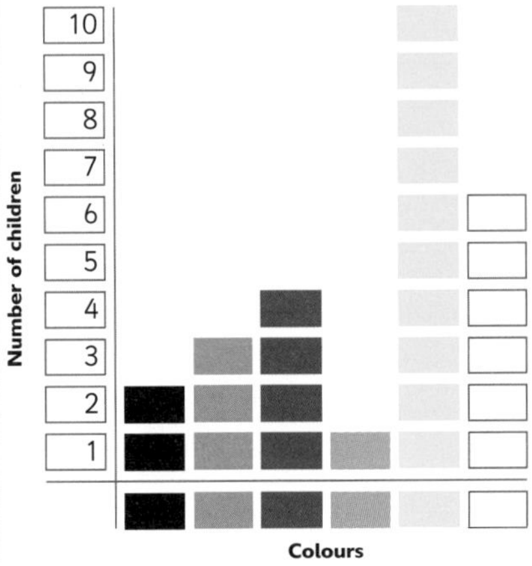

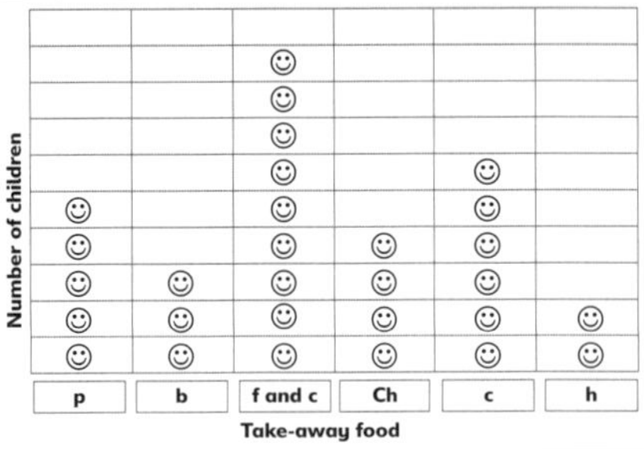